AESOP
In the Afternoon

AESOP

In the Afternoon

Albert Cullum

CITATION PRESS
NEW YORK
1972

Other Citation Press Books by Albert Cullum

PUSH BACK THE DESKS
SHAKE HANDS WITH SHAKESPEARE:
Eight Plays for Elementary Schools
GREEK TEARS AND ROMAN LAUGHTER:
Ten Tragedies and Five Comedies for Schools

To a back porch of summer memories…

GRATEFUL ACKNOWLEDGMENT IS MADE TO NORMA MILLAY ELLIS FOR PERMISSION TO REPRINT "SECOND FIG" BY EDNA ST. VINCENT MILLAY FROM COLLECTED POEMS, HARPER & ROW. COPYRIGHT 1922, 1950 BY EDNA ST. VINCENT MILLAY.

PUBLISHED BY CITATION PRESS, LIBRARY AND TRADE DIVISION, SCHOLASTIC MAGAZINES, INC., EDITORIAL OFFICE: 50 WEST 44 STREET, NEW YORK, NEW YORK 10036.

LIBRARY OF CONGRESS CATALOG CARD NUMBER: 73–181473
STANDARD BOOK NUMBER: 590–09535–8

PRINTED IN THE U.S.A.
Second printing, 1973

Foreword

Educators everywhere, awake! What the world needs now is a task force of *transitioners!*

What is a transitioner? The word comes from a combination of the words "translator" and "practitioner." And, a transitioner is exactly what the combination implies: he is a person (preferably a teacher) who has the ability to take any one of the thousands of ideas or theories currently running rampant in the area of creativity and translate that idea into actual practice in the classroom. A super transitioner is one who can come up with *his own* ideas and put them into practice!

Great and new ideas in educational endeavor are often lost because of want of a transitioner. The explosion of knowledge and the development of new concepts in the area of creativity are two such cases in point. Research findings have bombarded the minds of imaginative teachers everywhere. Challenges pour forth from the findings of this research at breakneck speed. New findings beget new theories. What would happen, for instance, if great value and stress were placed on developing the creative behaviors of children rather than the academic ones? Can the reservoir of creative thinking imprisoned in each human mind be released if divergent thinking processes are developed in classrooms as much as convergent thinking? What might happen if conditions were such in each classroom that thinking processes were structured to creative problem-solving activities? The challenges come fast, faster than transitioners are able to incorporate them into classroom practice.

Al Cullum is a super transitioner. Anyone who has read *Push Back the Desks, Shake Hands With Shakespeare,* or *Greek Tears and Roman Laughter* knows this. And now he has added another book of practical, useful ideas to develop one aspect of creative ability in children: *Aesop in the Afternoon.* It is sound in its philosophy, yet fun enough to bring the children back early from lunch!

In this delightful collection of dramatizations of Aesop's fables, Mr. Cullum illustrates that a sound approach to indirect, child-centered teaching is classroom theater where the skills taught during the morning can be meaningfully applied in creative problem-solving, (in the afternoons, of course). These carefully chosen plays present children with the main themes of life, they provide them a chance to explore personal problems, and they open new vistas for creative thinking. Mr. Cullum presents classroom theater in such a manner that any teacher can use it in its minimum form but with maximum results.

I tried some of Mr. Cullum's Aesop playlets one afternoon in an elementary school. I can assure you that what he says about his plays is absolutely so, especially if his suggestion for staging, "The children will have ideas of their own," is taken seriously. How true! They did!

I urge teachers everywhere to put away those dull workbooks in the afternoon. Substitute Aesop! Become a transitioner!

James A. Smith, Professor
State University College
Oswego, New York
December, 1971

Contents

Classroom Drama Enhances the Learning Process

Winston Churchill once said, "I always enjoyed learning but found it extremely distasteful being told how to learn!" Perhaps this is exactly what many girls and boys in many classrooms are saying to themselves. Perhaps students are silently wondering, "Why does school always have to be like school?"

True, much learning does take place directly, but why not practice *indirect teaching* during the afternoon hours? What is indirect teaching? It is simply a classroom structure the teacher establishes in which children are allowed to exhibit leadership and initiative and are given an opportunity to solve problems that arise from their own actions. Why not put the basic skills taught in the morning into action during the afternoons? Indirectly, of course!

A good approach to indirect, child-centered teaching is classroom theater. Classroom theater can be as effective as the television commercials children love—direct, brief, and interesting, with a "bang" ending! Many elementary classroom teachers throughout the country have discovered this type of learning activity to be most effective. Dramatic experiences have ranged from puppet shows to Shakespeare, from Greek tragedy to Roman comedy, from poetry to role-playing, from fairly tales to plays the class has written.

The plays in *Aesop in the Afternoon* are simple to present for they require very little practice, and they have been designed especially for classroom use in grades two through five—no stage or auditorium are required. Small groups of children will need approximately twenty minutes to prepare a presentation and five to ten minutes to perform it. The presentation can be followed by a stimulating fifteen minutes of classroom discussion.

Children are natural actors, even the shy, or seemingly shy, ones. Quite often I have discovered that seemingly shy, quiet children have more depth than extroverted ones. Children at a very young age create their own sense of theater, their own sense of drama via toys and imaginary friends; most certainly they communicate with their friendly and mean-monster acquaintances. Children establish a fantastically direct communication with animals—live or stuffed. They identify strongly with animals, and they seem to understand each others' language. Most of the plays in *Aesop in the Afternoon* have animal characters, and the situations will give a school child a feeling of comfort and reality. The plays will help bring children's home worlds into the classroom for the activities encourage them to pantomine gestures and imitate the sounds and actions of familiar animals.

Plays can introduce a sense of formal theater without suppressing student creativity. Children need constant reminders that they have the ability to create. Plays will expose students to main themes of life, but most important, if they are given an opportunity, they will expose their personalities. Even more vital, plays presented in the classroom will give students an awareness of themselves. Isn't that the whole purpose of education—to gain an awareness of ourselves? A liking of ourselves? A belief in ourselves? *Children deserve this kind of atmosphere of awareness.*

Psychologists have proved that more learning takes place in an atmosphere of emotional involvement than in a rigid clinical one. Children learn with and from each other. Meaningful learning takes place in a comfortable atmosphere . . . an atmosphere that encourages students to step into the unknown . . . an atmosphere that encourages students to take risks . . . an atmosphere of togetherness, where there is no right or wrong.

A class can be a family unit where individual needs are recognized; however, often the family needs to sit together, to laugh together, to discuss together, to decide together, and to create together! Classroom discussions, compromises, lack of compromise, and defense of individual beliefs are true learning experiences. They are learning experiences that deal with the *now* of students' lives, not some vague fragment of the future. A classroom is a true classroom when "slow learners" work with "quick learners," when students assume initiative, when leaders emerge, when learning to be a follower sometimes is necessary. A classroom is a healthy classroom when each student senses *the togetherness of the group without sacrificing his individual needs or uniqueness.*

There is a great need for more togetherness of students in elementary school classrooms. More teachers need to assume the role of advisor and resource person rather than instructor and authority figure. Teachers teach best by what they reflect. Teachers can reflect trust in a student committee, teachers can reflect belief in student decisions and interpretations, teachers can reflect pride in their students. It is essential that classrooms become more student-oriented, at least during the afternoons. A few plays each afternoon would make the afternoons ever so short. (Well, if not every afternoon, what about every other afternoon or the last hour of each afternoon?) Plays are packed with learning experiences —significant learning experiences!

Aesop in the Afternoon furnishes students and teachers with a wide choice of short plays that can be readily performed. Although the plays have been adapted from the fables of an early storyteller, they deal with age-old situations and reflect the *now* of things—a *now* that has a beginning, a middle, and an end. The plays have been arranged by the number of characters involved: plays for two characters, three characters, four characters, five characters, and six characters. They are brief and can involve the entire class. Through class discussion after each presentation, everyone becomes a participant—the audience as well as the performers. The plays have been expressly designed to set up learning situations in an indirect manner.

The *corners* of a classroom can become *centers* of learning, for here students can face the challenge of working together on their presentations without the teacher's help. In the corners of the room students can read together, look up words together, make decisions and judgments together—all the basic skills so essential to the art of living. Furthermore, in those classroom corners boys and girls will be attempting to utilize the basic skills taught in the morning. Of course, not every corner group will automatically achieve instant success, but the teacher with constant high expectations of his students will soon realize that the corners of his classroom need him less and less as the school year progresses.

These short plays are ideal for elementary school students. They will learn quickly new speaking and reading vocabulary because the words in the plays will make sense to them—emotional sense. In a very short time students will be comfortable with their lines and ready for a classroom presentation. And, perhaps most exciting of all, the teacher will discover that he has a creative classroom because he gave his children an opportunity to create. Perhaps the greatest thing teachers can do for children is to give them an opportunity to create. Through classroom drama, you will discover a uniqueness about your students for they will share with you a delightful sense of humor, a remarkable sense of the dramatic, and a depth they do not show during morning drills in basic skills. Given the opportunity after the presentations, students will display their abilities as philosophers, for Aesop presents many problems of living meaningful to all ages. Given the opportunity your students will share genuine emotions with you; you will be amazed at the depth they possess. I was!

Aesop in the Afternoon will help teachers develop a

rapport with their classes, a rapport of mutual respect for each other. Theater is a basic emotional structure for learning, for theater has been a cultural element of all nations and races, beginning with the tribal storyteller and continuing to the most avant garde theater of today. For centuries the people of the world have used theater as a cathartic experience. I have discovered again and again—in the ghetto, in suburbia, with the mentally retarded, the emotionally disturbed, the genius child, and with thousands and thousands of average children —that *all* need some moments of catharsis, even if only for a moment in a corner in an afternoon classroom. Roaring like a wounded lion, flying about a classroom like an eagle, or chasing an imaginary enemy around the desks offer exhilarating moments of catharsis.

The art of teaching in its most simple terms is the art of changing busy work and seat work into a meaningful experience for each boy and girl. *All teachers can do this!* In each classroom there is a fantastic amount of talent ready to express itself, and the teacher is the key person in allowing this talent and energy to emerge. Never have I discovered that the academic standards of a school were lowered by creating an atmosphere of theater in the classroom. In fact, again and again in my experience the standards of the school were raised and enhanced.

Your students look to you for encouragement and support, and we teachers have no right to deprive them of these expectations. School must be a meaningful emotional experience each day for each child, even if only for a moment. Without this essential emotional involvement, students develop doubts about the value of school, and then death at an early age does indeed occur.

Fortunately some elementary school teachers have a keen understanding of Edna St. Vincent Millay's poem, "Second Fig."

> On the ground your ugly houses stand,
> Come see my castles built upon the sand!

Involved elementary school teachers know that a certain amount of sand castles are needed in every classroom. Good elementary school teachers sense a need among their students for pretending, fantasy, and improvisation of stories. During my many years of elementary school teaching, I have yet to encounter a child who did not benefit by a touch of classroom theater.

Classroom theater in its simplest form—without costumes, without scenery, without makeup—establishes a truly child-oriented classroom. When children are allowed to be themselves, they are really unique. When they are given the opportunity to express *their* instinctive, intuitive sense of dramatic structure, your students will not disappoint you. They might even nominate you for the teacher of the year award!

Plays for Two Students

The Peacock
and the Crane

Characters   A Peacock
A Crane

Setting   Along the edge of a woods.

PEACOCK   Everyone look at me! Look at my beautiful feathers! Look at my brilliant colors! Truly I am beautiful! Yes, I am the most beautiful bird in these woods! I am so beautiful that I am envied by all the other birds!

CRANE   Are you still admiring yourself?

PEACOCK   And why not! I am robed as a king! Just

look at the gold and purple in my feathers! Are they not just like the colors that a king wears?

CRANE   Yes, they are pretty.

PEACOCK   Pretty you say? Pretty? I am magnificent! I have all the colors of the rainbow in my feathers.

CRANE   Yes, you do have many colors.

PEACOCK   But poor you! You are so pale looking. You don't even have a tiny bit of color on your wings. You are so very, very pale. Poor you!

CRANE   What you say about me is very true, Mr. Peacock. However, let me tell you something about myself that you might not know.

PEACOCK   What could you possibly have that would be better than anything I have?

CRANE   I can do something that you can't do.

PEACOCK   And what is that?

CRANE   I can fly up to the heavens and talk to the stars! All you can do is strut about on the ground. Keep your pretty feathers, Mr. Peacock. I will stay a bird who can fly!

Moral   Fine feathers don't always make fine birds.

Suggestions for staging
Encourage the peacock to really strut.
Encourage the crane to fly about the whole room with imaginary wide-spread wings.

The Wolf
and the Mountain Goat

Characters   A Wolf
           A Mountain Goat

Setting   A high cliff where a mountain goat is
          eating; below her a wolf is looking up.

WOLF   This has been a bad day for me for I have
    not been able to catch one creature for my
    breakfast. I am very hungry! I wonder if I can
    convince that mountain goat to come down off
    her cliff to my level? Then I will pounce upon
    her! Hello, Mrs. Goat! Say, can you hear me
    way up on your cliff?

23

GOAT Yes, I can hear you. What do you want, Mr. Wolf?

WOLF Oh, I don't want anything. I was just worried about you way up there on your high cliff. Aren't you afraid that you might slip and fall?

GOAT I don't think I will fall.

WOLF But if you do fall, you would break your leg. That would be a very painful injury, Mrs. Goat!

GOAT Thank you for your concern, Mr. Wolf, but I'm perfectly safe up here.

WOLF But Mrs. Goat, the grass is much greener down here. Think of that.

GOAT The grass up here is good enough for me, Mr. Wolf.

WOLF But Mrs. Goat, the grass down here is the best grass in the world!

GOAT Thank you again, Mr. Wolf, you are very kind to think about me.

WOLF Are you sure you won't change your mind, Mrs. Goat?

GOAT I'm quite sure that I won't change my mind.

WOLF Why, Mrs. Goat?

GOAT I know you too well, Mr. Wolf, to be tricked by you. You really don't care what I'm having for breakfast. You are only thinking about your own breakfast, and if I come down off my cliff, I will become your breakfast.

WOLF Don't you trust me, Mrs. Goat?

GOAT Thank you again for your kind invitation, Mr. Wolf, but I don't think I will accept it.

Moral　Check all invitations before you accept them.

Suggestions for staging
Encourage the wolf to speak in a very sweet voice.
The mountain cliff can be a chair on a table.

The Mouse
and the Bull

Characters   A Mouse
A Bull

Setting   Near a farmhouse.

MOUSE   There is Mr. Bull sound asleep in the pasture. I think I will go and bite him on the leg! *Mouse slowly creeps up to the sleeping bull and gives him a sharp bite on his leg.*

BULL   OUCH! OUCH! That hurt! I'll get you back, you mean Mouse! *Bull chases the mouse, but the mouse runs safely into his small hole in the farmhouse.* You can't hide from me, Mr. Mouse, for I am strong and powerful! I will knock down the wall to your little hole and eat you up! *He snorts and snorts and then charges the wall, but all he does is hurt his head! The bull charges the wall again and again, and finally is so tired he stops.*

I know what I will do. . . . I will rest right near your hole, Mr. Mouse, and catch you when you come out. I will wait all day just to get even with you. I am a strong and powerful bull, and I will destroy you when I catch you!

He waits and waits but soon falls asleep and begins to snore.

MOUSE   Listen to Mr. Bull snore! I will sneak out of my hole very very quietly and bite his leg again!

He slowly creeps out of his hole and bites the bull very hard on the same leg, and then quickly scampers back to the safety of his hole.

BULL   OUCH! OUCH! OUCH! That hurt!

He goes back to the pasture crying about his bitten leg.

Moral   There are times when the small and lowly can do more mischief than the strong and mighty.

Suggestions for staging

The hole in the farmhouse wall can be the opening of the teacher's desk or the wastepaper basket.

The mouse should creep slowly to bite the bull. The bull's snorts and snores should be very loud and he should cry loudly as he returns to his pasture.

The Grasshopper
and the Owl

Characters   An Owl
               A Grasshopper

Setting   Daytime in the forest. An owl is rest-
            ing in his hole in a tree, and the grass-
            hopper is on the grass below him.

GRASSHOPPER   Chirp! Chirp! Chirp! Chirp! Chirp!
Chirp! Chirp! Chirp! Chirp! Chirp! Chirp!
OWL   Miss Grasshopper, may I ask a favor of you?
GRASSHOPPER   Certainly. What favor?
OWL   As you know, I'm an owl. All owls stay awake
all night and sleep all day, so would you mind

going someplace else to do your chirping. I am trying to rest.

GRASSHOPPER But I like chirping in this spot! Chirp! Chirp! Chirp! Chirp! Chirp! Chirp! Chirp!

OWL Miss Grasshopper!

GRASSHOPPER Yes, Mr. Owl?

OWL This is a very, very big forest. Why can't you chirp somewhere else! Certainly in such a big forest there must be another spot that you would like.

GRASSHOPPER No, this is the only place in the whole forest that I like. Chirp! Chirp! Chirp! Chirp! Chirp! Chirp! Chirp! Chirp!

OWL Miss Grasshopper!

GRASSHOPPER Yes, Mr. Owl?

OWL If this is the only place you like to chirp, then may I ask you another favor?

GRASSHOPPER Certainly, Mr. Owl. What is it?

OWL Would you mind chirping with a very soft voice?

GRASSHOPPER No, I always chirp in a loud voice because my chirp is so beautiful! Chirp! Chirp! Chirp! Chirp! Chirp!

OWL Miss Grasshopper!

GRASSHOPPER Yes, Mr. Owl?

OWL Come to think of it, you do have a lovely chirp. You probably have the most beautiful chirp in the whole forest.

GRASSHOPPER Why, thank you Mr. Owl. How nice of you to say so.

OWL Yes, I'm sure it's the most beautiful chirp in the whole world.

GRASSHOPPER Thank you, thank you, Mr. Owl. Chirp! Chirp! Chirp! Chirp! Chirp! Chirp! Chirp!

OWL Since I cannot sleep because of your beautiful chirp, why don't you fly up to my hole in the tree and visit me. I have some delicious nectar given to me by the gods that I will share with you. The delicious nectar will match the sweetness of your voice.

GRASSHOPPER Thank you, Mr. Owl. I accept your kind invitation.

The grasshopper flies up to the hollow of the tree and the owl gobbles her up.

Moral If you bother others all the time, you can get into trouble.

Suggestions for staging.
The owl can be seated high on a chair on a table.
The grasshopper's chirp should be loud and clear and she should be encouraged to hop about while chirping.
The owl can cover the grasshopper with a blanket or large piece of cloth to show she has been gobbled up.

The Wolf
and the House Dog

Characters   A Wolf
            A Dog

Setting   Near a woods.

WOLF   How wonderful you look! You are fat and
sleek, while I am all skin and bones. I hunt day
and night for food in these woods and most of
the time I starve. How is it you don't have the
same problem?

DOG   You could be in just as great a shape as I am.

WOLF   What do you mean?

DOG   Well, I eat regularly every day, and on holidays I get extra treats!

WOLF   I still don't know what you are talking about!

DOG   I am fed every day because I guard my master's house and keep thieves away.

WOLF   You mean to say you get fed every day just for guarding your master's house?

DOG   Very true! He treats me very nicely and pets me often. Come with me and I'll show you the house I guard.

WOLF   Yes, I would like to see the house you guard. But, say, what is that mark around your neck?

DOG   Oh that! That's nothing. That's the mark from the collar my master places around my neck when he chains me up at night.

WOLF   You mean to tell me that you are chained?

DOG   Yes. What is wrong with that?

WOLF   You mean to tell me that you are not free to come and go as you like? You mean to tell me that you can't roam whenever and wherever you choose?

DOG   Not when my master chains me up.

WOLF   Then good-bye my friend.

DOG   Say, where are you running off to?

WOLF   I may be all skin and bones but at least I'm free to come and go as I please. Good-bye!

Moral   No one loves chains though they be made of gold.

Suggestions for staging
Use the whole room.
When the wolf leaves, his voice should sound far away.

The Lion
and the Bull

Characters   A Lion
A Bull

Setting   Near the edge of a forest.

LION   That's a beautiful bull in the pasture. I sure
would like to have him for my dinner, but he's
so big that I'm afraid to attack him. Perhaps I
can trick him into coming into my cave where
I'll have a better chance of capturing him.
Hello, Mr. Bull!

BULL   Hello, Mr. Lion. How are you today?

LION   Fine, thank you. What are you doing?

BULL   Oh, just grazing. Why?

LION   Well, I have just killed a sheep, and I thought perhaps you would like to come home and share it with me. It's nice and tender, and you will enjoy the meal.

BULL   Why are you asking me to share the sheep with you? Why don't you eat it all by yourself?

LION   I'm asking you because you are my friend. Will you come?

BULL   Why, yes, I think I will.

They walk into the forest to the entrance of the lion's den.

LION   Well, here we are at last. Why are you backing away, Mr. Bull?

BULL   I'm backing away because I don't see the sheep you promised. All I see is a large fire and a big pot. I have a feeling that I'm the sheep you are talking about.

LION   I don't know what you're talking about.

BULL   I know what I'm talking about! Good-bye, Mr. Lion. Perhaps some other day I'll have dinner with you.

Moral   Look before you enter.

Suggestions for staging
The wastepaper basket can be the cooking pot the bull sees.
The lion and bull can stroll about the classroom on the way to the lion's den.

The Two Frogs

Characters   First Frog
               Second Frog

Setting   A very, very hot summer day. The two
frogs are hopping along a very, very
dusty road.

FIRST FROG We have been hopping along all day,
and I don't think we will ever find water! Every
pond is all dried up!

SECOND FROG Don't get discouraged! After all, this
has been a very dry summer. Of course, it will
take some time before we find a nice wet pond.
*The two frogs continue hopping down the dry
dusty road.*

FIRST FROG Look! Look! There's a well! At last our
journey is over!
Both frogs jump to the edge of the well.
Let's jump in! It looks so nice and wet!

SECOND FROG   Wait! Wait! Don't jump in!

FIRST FROG   Don't be silly. Why not?

SECOND FROG   Let's talk about it first.

FIRST FROG   There is nothing to talk about. All day long we have been hopping along this hot dusty road searching for water. Now we have found it, and you say, let's talk about it! I'm going to jump!

SECOND FROG   Wait a moment!

FIRST FROG   I'm going to jump into the well right now!

SECOND FROG   Wait! Wait! Yes, the well is full of cool delicious water, but what if the well goes dry just as all the other ponds went dry? We would be in a dreadful situation for we wouldn't be able to get out of the well!

FIRST FROG   Don't be silly! The well isn't going to go dry.

SECOND FROG   You jump in if that's your decision, but as for me I'm going to keep hopping along the hot dusty road until I find a cool stream. Good-bye!

Moral   Think twice before you leap.

Suggestions for staging
The long dusty road can be the whole classroom. The well can be three or four desks placed close together with an opening in the center for the frog to jump into.

The Fox
and the Crow

Characters   A Fox
             A Crow

Setting   A spot in a forest.

CROW   Wow! I see a big piece of cheese that someone must have dropped accidentally. What luck!
I will fly down and grab it.
*He flies down from the tree, snatches the piece
of cheese, and flies back to his lofty branch.*

FOX *(whispering)*   Is that Mr. Crow with a delicious
piece of cheese in his mouth? I certainly would
like to have that tasty piece of cheese for my

breakfast! How can I get that piece of cheese from Mr. Crow? I don't know how to climb trees so I can't grab it from him, and even if I knew how to climb trees, he would fly away with the piece of cheese in his mouth. The only way I can get the piece of cheese from Mr. Crow is by using my wits. . . . My plan is to make Mr. Crow speak and when he speaks, he will drop the piece of cheese right into my mouth! (*loudly*) Good morning, Mr. Crow. Nice day today isn't it? How beautiful you look this bright early morn! Your eyes are so shiny! Your plumes look so lovely in the morning sun. You know something? You are the most beautiful creature in the forest. Yes, you are! Tell me something. Can you sing? If I could only hear you sing, then I would surely believe you were the fairest creature of all. If I could hear you sing, there would be no doubt in my mind at all. Then I would be certain that you were the finest bird in the world!

The crow struts proudly up and down his branch.

FOX   Yes, all crows are lovely, but you are the loveliest of them all. If you can sing as beautifully as you look, I'm sure you must be the most beautiful creature in the world.

CROW   Caw! Caw! Caw! . . . Oh dear, I lost my lovely piece of cheese!

The fox gobbles up the cheese.

FOX   Here is some good advice, Mr. Crow . . .

Don't let sweet words fool you. Good-bye, Mr. Crow, and thank you for that delicious piece of cheese.

Moral Flattery works on all of us.

Suggestions for staging
A chair upon a table will work nicely as the branch for the crow.
The crow should cry and the fox show much happiness at the end.

The Man
and the Satyr

Characters   A Man
A Satyr

Setting   In a house.

MAN   Let us have a glass of wine together and swear
to be friends forever!

SATYR   Agreed.

They drink the wine.

MAN   My, it certainly is getting cold out!

SATYR   It looks like a big storm is approaching.

MAN   I think I had better make a fire.

SATYR   I'll get some wood.

MAN   Hurry, for it's getting colder and colder each
moment.

The satyr runs out and returns with some wood.
The man is blowing on his hands.

SATYR   Why do you blow on your hands that way?

MAN   I blow on my hands to warm them up.

SATYR   Oh, I see. Now I understand.

They place the wood in the fireplace and start a fire.

MAN   I think it's time to have supper, don't you?

SATYR   Yes, I am very hungry.

MAN   Good! Let's put the soup on the table.

SATYR   It smells delicious!

They sit down to eat, and the man blows on the soup.

Why do you blow on the soup that way?

MAN   I blow on the soup to cool it off.

SATYR   I don't understand. Earlier you blew on your hands to warm them up, and now with the same breath you blow on the soup to cool it off!

MAN   That's correct.

SATYR   I really don't understand, but this I know . . . I no longer consider you a friend.

MAN   What do you mean?

SATYR   A person who with the same breath blows hot and cold can't be much of a trusted friend!

Moral   Good friends are constant.

Suggestions for staging
The teacher's desk can be the supper table.
An imaginary fireplace and imaginary plates will suffice.

The Wolf
and the Lamb

Characters   A Wolf
              A Lamb

Setting   Near a brook in a woods on a very hot
           summer day.

WOLF   I see a little lamb standing in the brook. I
       want to eat her up, but she is such a nice little
       lamb that I know I really shouldn't. But I do
       want to eat her up so I'll start an argument with
       her and that will make me angry and give me an
       excuse to gobble her up!
       He goes down to the brook.
       Little lamb, get out of my brook! You are mak-

ing the water muddy so that I cannot enjoy my drink!

LAMB   But that's not true, for the brook is running downhill from where you stand, Mr. Wolf.

WOLF   Yes, you are right. But what are you doing drinking my water? How dare you drink my water!

LAMB   But that's not true, Mr. Wolf, for I still drink only my mother's milk. I have not tasted your water.

WOLF   Yes, you are right again. But you are a bad little lamb anyway for last year I heard you say mean things about me!

LAMB   But that's not true, Mr. Wolf, for I am less than a year old. I was not born a year ago!

WOLF   Yes, you are right again! But all you sheep and lambs have the same dull kind of faces, and if it was not you who said bad, mean things about me, then it must have have been your older brother, and that is excuse enough for me to eat you up!

The wolf gobbles up the lamb.

Moral   An evil person will find any excuse to do evil.

Suggestions for staging
A long piece of paper can be the **brook**.
The lamb can yell and scream as the wolf eats her **up**.

44

The Boy
and the Nuts

Characters   A Mother
   A Boy

Setting   In a house.

BOY   Mother, what are you carrying in the jar?

MOTHER   Some nuts, my son. Would you like some?

BOY   Oh yes, I love nuts! May I have as big a handful as I like?

MOTHER   You may have as big a handful as you can
   take.

   *The boy sticks his hand in the jar and grabs all
   the nuts his fist can hold.*

BOY   But Mother, I can't get my hand out!

MOTHER   Let some of the nuts go, and you will be
   able to pull out your hand.

BOY   No! No! No! I want a big handful of nuts!
The boy begins to cry because he can't get his hand out of the jar.

MOTHER   There is no need to cry. Just let go of some of the nuts and your hand will come out.

BOY   No! No! No! It's a mean old jar that won't let my hand out!

MOTHER   It's not the jar, my son. It is you! You are very, very greedy!

BOY   No! No! No! It's the jar's fault.

MOTHER   Listen, my son, be satisfied with half as many nuts, and you will be able to get your hand out.

Moral   Do not attempt too much at once.

Suggestions for staging
An imaginary jar is sufficient.
Much loud crying from the boy . . . a temper tantrum!

The Flea
and the Ox

Characters   A Flea
         An Ox

Setting   A barnyard.

FLEA   I really don't understand you, Mr. Ox!

OX   What seems to be bothering you, Miss Flea?

FLEA   Well, here you are, big and strong, and yet
        you slave for your owner day in and day out.
        You pull his wagons and plow his fields even
        though you are big and strong and could tell
        him NO!

OX   Yes, I work hard for my owner.

FLEA   Look at me, Mr. Ox! I'm very small and weak, and yet I feed on your owner's flesh and drink his blood without doing any hard work!

OX   I understand what you are saying, Miss Flea, but I really don't mind working for my owner.

FLEA   How can you say such a thing!

OX   I am well fed by my owner, and he also likes me very much. Sometimes he even pats me on the head and tells me how good I am.

FLEA   Oh dear! Oh dear! This patting on the head you like is bad for me. Whenever I get patted on the head, it brings about my destruction!

Moral   Loyalty is well rewarded.

Suggestions for staging
The flea should hop around a great deal.
The ox should be peacefully resting, chewing his cud.

The Donkey
and the Wolf

Characters A Donkey
             A Wolf

Setting A meadow.

DONKEY I think I see that mean Mr. Wolf creeping around the meadow. I don't think he is up to any good. I had better be careful because I think he is planning to attack me. I must think of some plan to get myself out of this situation. . . . I know! I will pretend to be lame.

WOLF I think Mr. Donkey looks lame. This is a good time to prepare my attack! . . . Hello, Mr. Donkey! What seems to be the trouble? Your back leg seems to be hurting you.

DONKEY   Yes, you are right. I just stepped on a sharp thorn, and it hurts very much!

WOLF   Let me get closer and perhaps I can be of help.

DONKEY   Oh, Mr. Wolf, I am afraid you want to eat me up. I am lame and cannot run away from you. Alas, poor me. . . . If you are going to eat me though, you had better pull the thorn out of my foot first so that it won't stick in your throat when you gobble me up.

WOLF   That makes good sense. Yes, I'll remove the thorn.

When the wolf gets close to the back leg, the donkey gives him a hard kick in the head and runs away.

Moral   Stick to your objectives and don't be sidetracked.

Suggestions for staging
When the donkey pretends to be lame, he can limp around.
As the wolf talks to the donkey, he should slowly creep closer.
The wolf can howl and cry when he is kicked.

The Wild Boar
and the Fox

Characters   A Boar
           A Fox

Setting   The middle of a forest.

BOAR   Now that I have a moment, I think I will
sharpen my teeth. Here is a nice sturdy tree that
will help me.
*The boar rubs and rubs his tusks against the
very hard tree trunk.*
FOX   What in the world are you doing, Mr. Boar?
BOAR   I'm sharpening my tusks.

FOX   That seems like a very silly thing to be doing.

BOAR   Really! why?

FOX   It's silly for I don't see any danger about. I don't see a hunter and his dogs coming after you!

BOAR   I don't see a hunter and his dogs coming after me either.

FOX   Well, then, why all the nonsense about sharpening your tusks?

BOAR   Mr. Fox, I don't think you are too bright today. Wouldn't it be foolish of me to wait until the hunter and his dogs attacked before I sharpened my tusks? I think you are foolish, Mr. Fox, not I!

Moral   It pays to be prepared.

Suggestions for staging
The boar can grunt and strain as he sharpens his tusks.
The teacher's desk can be the sturdy tree trunk.

The Eagle
and the Hawk

Characters   An Eagle
            A Hawk

Setting   The high branch of a tree.

EAGLE   Oh! Oh! Oh dear. I feel so sad today! So very sad! Poor me!

HAWK   You look so sad today, Miss Eagle. Tell me why.

EAGLE   Boo-hoo! I have been looking for a mate for weeks, but no one will marry me! Oh, poor me!

HAWK   Why not marry me?

EAGLE   Marry you?

HAWK   I am stronger than you, and I will be able to supply you with much food.

EAGLE   Are you sure you will be able to find delicious food for me every day?

HAWK   Of course I'm sure, lovely Miss Eagle. Why,

53

just the other day I picked up a huge ostrich
with my talons and carried him off into the sky!

EAGLE   My, my! You must be very strong indeed,
Mr. Hawk!

HAWK   Yes, I'm sure I will be able to provide you
with good food every single day, Miss Eagle. Yes,
I'm very sure!

EAGLE   Very well, Mr. Hawk, I will marry you!
. . . Now that we are married fly off and bring
me a huge ostrich for I am hungry.

HAWK   Very well, my dear wife.
*The hawk flies off but comes back with only a
very little mouse.*

EAGLE   You call that an ostrich? To me it looks like
a very tiny mouse!

HAWK   Yes, I'm afraid that's all it is, a very tiny
mouse.

EAGLE   Is this the way you keep your promises to
me?

HAWK   I was afraid you would not marry me if I told
you the truth!

Moral   Some people will promise anything to
get their way.

Suggestions for staging
Two chairs on a large table can be the branch of
the tree.
The hawk should roam about the classroom
looking for food.

The Seaside Travelers

Characters   First traveler
Second traveler

Setting   A very high mountain overlooking the ocean.

FIRST TRAVELER   Look! Look! Isn't that something way out on the ocean?

SECOND TRAVELER   I wonder what it is?

FIRST TRAVELER   It looks like a huge ship!

SECOND TRAVELER   Yes, it is a ship! Look how large the sails are!

FIRST TRAVELER   It's a beauty of a ship!

SECOND TRAVELER   Let's go down to the harbor when it arrives.

FIRST TRAVELER   It will be exciting to visit such a beautiful vessel!

SECOND TRAVELER   It's coming closer, and I can see it better.

FIRST TRAVELER   So can I, and it doesn't seem to be a huge ship at all!

SECOND TRAVELER   You are right! It doesn't have any sails!

FIRST TRAVELER   You know what it is? It's just an old rowboat!

SECOND TRAVELER   How disappointing! It's just a rowboat drifting toward shore.

FIRST TRAVELER   Let's rush down the mountain and see what's in it!

SECOND TRAVELER   Good idea! You know, we might find something valuable in a drifting rowboat!

FIRST TRAVELER   Let's hurry down the mountain!
  The two travelers rush down the steep mountain running breathlessly to the edge of the water.

SECOND TRAVELER   Another disappointment! It's only a bunch of large sticks tied together!

Moral   Wishful thinking can be disappointing.

Suggestions for staging
Two chairs on a table will serve as a high mountain.

When rushing down to the ocean, the two travelers should be encouraged to make it a long trip down by using the whole area of the classroom.

Plays for Three Students

The Lion
and the Dolphin

Characters   A Lion
              A Dolphin
              A Bull

Setting   Near a seashore.

LION   Hello, Mr. Dolphin. Are you in the mighty
ocean?

DOLPHIN   Yes, here I am, Mr. Lion. What is the
matter?

LION   Well, I have been thinking. I am king of the
land, right?

DOLPHIN   Yes, you are correct.

LION   And you are king of the ocean, correct?

DOLPHIN   Yes, you are correct, Mr. Lion.

LION   Well, if I am king of the land and you are
king of the ocean, we ought to be the best of
friends.

DOLPHIN   I agree. Yes, let us be good friends.

BULL   I see a lion near the seashore. I think I will attack him and eat him for supper.

The bull charges toward the lion.

LION   HELP! HELP! Mr. Dolphin, help me! Help me, I pray!

DOLPHIN   Mr. Lion, I would like to help you, but my place is in the water. I am out of place and of no value on land.

LION   You are a traitor! I thought we were the best of friends, and yet you refuse to help me against this bull.

DOLPHIN   You don't understand, Mr. Lion. I am not a traitor. If I could help you, I would, but, alas, nature never gave me the talent to live on land.

Moral   It's good to know what you can do and what you cannot do.

Suggestions for staging

The lion could stand on a table while the dolphin is swimming on the floor.

The bull can make a great deal of noise as he is attacking the lion.

The Heron

Characters   A Heron
             A Perch
             A Catfish

Setting   Along the bank of a stream one early
          morning.

HERON   What a beautiful morning. I think I'll go
down to the stream and find myself a delicious
breakfast. I want something very special this
morning, . . . not any old breakfast, but a
breakfast fit for a king!

The heron wanders down to the stream.

PERCH   Aren't you going to eat me for breakfast this morning, Mr. Heron?

HERON   Go away! You, are much too small of a perch for me! Go away! This morning I want a breakfast fit for a king!

CATFISH   Good morning, Mr. Heron.

HERON   Good morning and stop annoying me.

CATFISH   But aren't you going to eat me for breakfast this morning?

HERON   Go away! Go away! Go away! You are much too bony. This morning I am looking for a breakfast fit for a king!

He strolls up and down the stream.

It is nearly noon for the sun is way up in the sky, and I still don't have my breakfast.

He continues to look but finds nothing.

It is beginning to get dark, and I am very hungry, but I can't find a thing to eat. Poor me, not even a tiny minnow. Boo-hoo!

Moral   He who is hard to please, may get nothing in the end.

Suggestions for staging

A long roll of paper can represent the stream.
The perch and the catfish should swim up to the heron and then disappear.
The heron should stroll proudly in the morning but by nighttime be quite tired and sad.

The Serpent
and the Eagle

Characters   A Serpent
                 An Eagle
                 A Farmer

Setting   The serpent and the eagle are having a fierce battle.

SERPENT   Now I have you about the neck, and I am going to strangle you, Mr. Eagle, until all the breath is out of you.

EAGLE   Help me! Someone help me!

FARMER Hold on for I will help you.

With much struggle the farmer removes the serpent from the eagle's neck, and the eagle flies away.

EAGLE Thank you, Mr. Farmer. Perhaps someday I will be able to help you.

SERPENT (*whispering*) I will get even with you, Mr. Farmer. You will regret having helped that eagle.

The serpent slithers over to the drinking cup of the farmer, spits his poison into it, and then slithers quietly away.

FARMER The sun is way up in the sky so it must be time to eat my lunch and drink my water. I am very thirsty so I will drink my water first.

THE EAGLE (*way up in a tree*) Oh no! I must stop Mr. Farmer from drinking the water for it has been poisoned by the venom of the serpent.

He swoops down from his tree and grabs the drinking cup with his talons, carrying it away.

Moral Revenge doesn't always work.

Suggestions for staging

The battle between the serpent and the eagle can be a very complicated one planned by the students.

Encourage the serpent to really slither.

Encourage the eagle to use the whole room as he flies and swoops.

The Horse
and the Donkey

Characters   A Horse
A Donkey
The Horse's owner

Setting   Along a country road.

HORSE   Get out of my way you silly looking donkey!
DONKEY   Can't you see I have heavy loads and that
it is difficult for me to move quickly?
HORSE   How dare you talk to me like that. You are
nothing but an ugly old donkey, while I am a
beautiful proud horse. Get out of my way!

DONKEY   Yes sir, I will move out of your way, but give me time for I am old and my load is heavy . . . very heavy!

HORSE   Hurry, or I will kick you in the heels!

DONKEY   I'm moving! I'm moving!

HORSE   Watch me go right by you, you silly looking donkey.

The horse gallops by the donkey flinging dust in his face.

The next day.

OWNER   You know something, my dear horse? I think you are getting old and I should get myself a new young powerful horse!

HORSE   Oh no, master! I am still a proud horse!

OWNER   You were, but now you are not. I'm going to have you join the donkey and carry heavy loads. You will not have to run so fast.

DONKEY   Well, well, well! If it isn't the fine proud horse who made fun of me yesterday. Now, who can you make fun of?

Moral   He who laughs last laughs best.

Suggestions for staging

The donkey and the horse should make use of the entire room.

The horse should be very proud and full of energy.

The donkey should be very old and weak.

Much laughter from the donkey at the end.

The Playful Donkey

Characters A Donkey
A Monkey
The Donkey's owner

Setting The roof of a farmhouse.

MONKEY Look at me, Mr. Donkey! Look at me! See how beautifully I can dance upon the rooftop.

DONKEY Yes, it seems to be a great deal of fun. I think I'll try it.

MONKEY I don't think you should try it, Mr. Donkey.

DONKEY Don't be silly. If you can do it, so can I . . . and perhaps even better!

MONKEY I wish you would change your mind.

DONKEY Out of my way! Watch me now!

The donkey begins to dance upon the rooftop, and the shingles begin to fall off.

OWNER   Get off that roof you stupid donkey! You are ruining my beautiful new roof!

DONKEY   But when you saw the monkey dance on your roof, you thought it was very funny, and you laughed and laughed.

OWNER   Get off, I say, before I come up there and knock you off. You are ruining my roof. GET OFF NOW!

DONKEY   But . . .

OWNER   Never mind what the monkey did . . . get off immediately.

Moral   It is foolish to try to imitate the skills of others.

Suggestions for staging
The top of a table can be the rooftop.
Both the monkey and the donkey should be encouraged to do much lively dancing.
The owner can shout and holler.

The Boy Who Went Into the River

Characters   A Boy
His Mother
A Man

Setting   Near a big river on a hot summer day.

MOTHER   Listen carefully, my son. I don't want you swimming in the river while I'm away. Do you understand?

BOY   Yes, Mother, I understand.

MOTHER   I will be back shortly. Good-bye my son, and remember to obey your mother. (*She leaves.*)

BOY   It's such a hot day, I think I'll just wet my feet.
. . . Oh, that feels so good! I think I will go in,
but just up to my waist. . . . Oooooh, that feels
so good. I think I'll go in just up to my neck.
. . . Help! Help! Help! Help! The water is
over my head, and the current is so swift I can't
get back to shore. Someone help me! Help!
Help! Help! Mister! Mister! Help me! I'm
drowning!

MAN   You are a very careless young boy for going
into such deep water!

BOY   I know! I know! But help me!

MAN   I'm sure you disobeyed your mother! Wait till
she finds out!

BOY   Yes, I disobeyed her, but help me! Help me!

MAN   You young people are very foolish at times.

BOY   Oh sir, please help me first and scold me after-
wards!

Moral   In a crisis, give help first, then advice.

Suggestions for staging
Large piece of cloth or long piece of paper can
represent the river.
Much yelling from the drowning boy.

Two Travelers
and a Bear

Characters First traveler
Second traveler
A Bear

Setting Along a path in a woods.

FIRST TRAVELER What a nice day to take a stroll through the woods. Aren't you glad you came along?

SECOND TRAVELER Yes, you were a good friend to invite me.

FIRST TRAVELER Yes, I am your best friend!

The bear growls loudly and stamps through the forest.

SECOND TRAVELER   What was that noise?

FIRST TRAVELER   Look over there! It's a huge bear!!!

SECOND TRAVELER   He's enormous and he looks very angry.

FIRST TRAVELER   Look, he sees us. He's starting to come this way.

SECOND TRAVELER   What shall we do?

FIRST TRAVELER   I don't know what you are going to do, but I'm climbing up on this tree branch so the bear can't reach me.

SECOND TRAVELER   There are no other trees around with low branches. Where can I hide?

FIRST TRAVELER   That's your problem. I know I'm safe from the bear. You will have to look after yourself. Sorry, my friend.

SECOND TRAVELER   I know what I will do. I will lie flat on the ground and pretend I am dead. I heard once that bears do not eat dead bodies.
The bear enters slowly growling loudly. He smells the body on the ground and then leaves.

FIRST TRAVELER   That certainly was a close call, but we both are safe.

SECOND TRAVELER   Yes, we both are safe.

FIRST TRAVELER   For a moment I thought the bear was whispering something in your ear. Did he?

SECOND TRAVELER   Yes, the bear did whisper something in my ear.

FIRST TRAVELER   You're joking?

SECOND TRAVELER   No, I'm not joking. The bear

told me to find another friend. He told me that
I don't need friends like you.

Moral   False friends leave you in time of trouble.

Suggestions for staging
A table will serve as a branch of the tree to climb
onto.
The bear should make many sounds.

The Crow
and Mercury

Characters A Crow
The god Apollo
The god Mercury

Setting In a forest.

CROW Help! Help me! Please someone help me!
Can't someone see I am caught in a snare! Why
doesn't someone help me! Where are all my
friends when I need them? . . . I know what
I will do! I will pray to the god Apollo for help.
Perhaps he will hear me and release me from
this snare. Oh mighty god Apollo, please look

upon me with favor and release me from this powerful snare. Oh mighty god Apollo, hear my plea! Please come and help me, Oh mighty Apollo! If you come and help me, I will hunt and hunt for the finest berries for you to eat.

APOLLO   I heard your plea and I am here! If I release you from the snare, what do you promise me?

CROW   Oh mighty Apollo, I promise to bring you the finest berries of the forest for you to eat. I promise! I promise!

APOLLO   Very well! I will now set you free from the snare.

The crow immediately flies away but soon he is caught in another snare.

CROW   I am trapped again! What shall I do! What shall I do! Help! Help! Someone come and help me. . . . No one answers! Poor me! . . . I know what I will do. I will pray to the god Mercury for help. He will hear me and release me from this powerful snare. Oh mighty Mercury, come and help a poor little crow trapped in a powerful snare. Oh mighty Mercury, hear my plea. Please come and help me! I promise to hunt and hunt for the finest berries of the forest for you to eat if you will help me!

MERCURY   I heard your plea, Mr. Crow. What is it you want me to do?

CROW   Please release me from this powerful snare.

MERCURY   If I release you from the powerful snare, what will you promise to bring me?

CROW   I promise to bring you the finest berries of the forest for you to eat.

MERCURY   But Mr. Crow, why should I believe you?

CROW   Because I made you a promise!

MERCURY   But Mr. Crow, your promises are false. I heard you last week make the same promise to Apollo, and you never kept your promise. You ate all the berries yourself.

CROW   Oh mighty Mercury, I will keep my promise this time!

MERCURY   I do not believe you, Mr. Crow, and I have decided not to release you from the powerful snare. Good-bye.

Moral   It is difficult to believe people who don't keep their promises.

Suggestions for staging
The snare can be the legs of a classroom desk.
The crow should fly about the room.
The gods Apollo and Mercury could be standing high on a desk above the crow.
Encourage the crow to cry and wail.

The Lion, the Wolf, and the Fox

Characters A Lion
           A Wolf
           A Fox

Setting In the cave of a lion in the forest.

LION I have been sick for weeks for I am getting old. How nice it was of all the animals of the forest to come and visit me. Their visits cheered me up, and I feel a little better. But I am still very weak and ill. Oh, so very ill! So very ill!

WOLF Just a moment, Mr. Lion. I wish to correct what you just said.

LION What do you mean, Mr. Wolf? What mistake did I make?

WOLF You said that all the animals of the forest came to visit you and to cheer you up, but that is not true!

LION I thought all the animals came to visit me.

WOLF All of them came, Mr. Lion, except one!

LION Who is that one, Mr. Wolf?

WOLF Mr. Fox has not visited you, nor does he care to visit!

LION This makes me very angry, and when I see Mr. Fox I will pounce upon him and eat him up!

At that moment the fox enters the lion's den. He has overheard all the wolf said.

FOX Hello, Mr. Lion.

LION I'm very angry with you, Mr. Fox, and I'm going to eat you up!

FOX But wait! Why are you going to eat me up?

LION Because you were the only animal of the forest who did not come to visit me when I was very ill.

FOX But wait, wait! Do you know why I didn't visit you?

LION You better have a good reason, or you will soon be in my stomach!

FOX Listen carefully, Mr. Lion.

LION Hurry and speak!

FOX I could not visit you because I was searching the forest trying to find a doctor who would give me a cure for your sickness.

LION   Oh! And did you find a cure for me?

FOX   Yes, I did.

LION   Tell me! Tell me! I wish to get better very soon.

FOX   The doctor told me to tell you that you will get better if you kill a wolf and wrap his skin around you.

The wolf attempts to run out of the cave, but the lion catches him, kills him, and wraps the skin around him.

Moral   If you can't speak well of a person, it's best not to say anything.

Suggestions for staging

The fox should listen carefully outside the cave.

The lion can groan a lot during his sickness.

Encourage much noise as the lion skins the wolf.

The wolf can wear a coat and the lion can use that for the skin.

The Dog, the Rooster,
and the Fox

Characters   A Dog
              A Rooster
              A Fox

Setting   In the middle of a woods.

DOG   Say, Mr. Rooster, let us take a long trip to-
    gether.
ROOSTER   Good idea! Let's go.
    The dog and the rooster start their trip.
DOG   We have walked many miles, and it is begin-

ning to get dark. Don't you think we should find a place to sleep?

ROOSTER   Good idea. I will fly up to that high branch and sleep. Where will you sleep?

DOG   I'll sleep in the hole at the bottom of the same tree.

ROOSTER   Sleep well, Mr. Dog. In the morning we will continue our journey.

DOG   Good night, Mr. Rooster.

Both the dog and the rooster sleep soundly.

ROOSTER   The sun is rising. I had better announce to the people that it is morning. Cock-a-doodle-do! COCK-A-DOODLE-DO! Time to get up! Time to begin your work! Everybody up!

FOX   That is a fine rooster crowing. Perhaps he will be my breakfast. Good morning, Mr. Rooster!

ROOSTER   Good morning, Mr. Fox.

FOX   Was that you I just heard crowing?

ROOSTER   Yes it was, Mr. Fox.

FOX   My, you have a beautiful voice. It is so loud and clear!

ROOSTER   Why thank you, Mr. Fox.

FOX   You crow so beautifully that I would like to be your friend.

ROOSTER   Why thank you, Mr. Fox.

FOX   Why don't you come down so we can have a chat?

ROOSTER   I have a better idea. Why don't you come up. Go around to the back of tree and you will find a hole in the trunk. Wake up my friend and he will let you in.

FOX   Thank you, Mr. Rooster. I know we are going to be great friends!
The fox goes to the back of the tree, and the dog pounces upon him.

Moral   Liars often set up their own traps.

Suggestions for staging
A table can serve as a tree.
The rooster should be encouraged to crow loudly.
The fight between the dog and the fox can be a long or short one.
The cast can decide whether the dog kills the fox or chases it away.

The Goose Who Laid
the Golden Eggs

Characters   A Goose
A Farmer
The Farmer's Wife

Setting   A barnyard early one morning.

FARMER   Time to go and gather the eggs. Where are
you, my beautiful goose?
GOOSE   Here I am, master.
FARMER   How many eggs do you have for me this
morning, my beautiful goose?
GOOSE   Just one as usual.

FARMER But wait! What is this? Your egg this morning is yellow and very heavy. Is this some joke you are playing on me?

GOOSE No, master. It is not a joke.

FARMER But your egg this morning is of pure gold! Do you hear me? Pure gold!

GOOSE Yes, master, I know.

FARMER Wife! Wife! Come here quickly! Wife, I say come here quickly!

WIFE What are you yelling about?

FARMER Look! Look! A solid golden egg!

WIFE Oh how wonderful! How wonderful!

The next morning.

FARMER Time to go and gather the eggs. Where are you, my beautiful, beautiful, beautiful goose?

GOOSE Here I am, master.

FARMER How many eggs do you have for me this morning?

GOOSE Just one as usual.

FARMER I don't believe it! Another golden egg! Oh, you truly are a beautiful, beautiful, beautiful goose!

GOOSE Thank you, master.

FARMER Wife! Wife! Come quickly!

WIFE Another golden egg! How lovely!

FARMER (*whispering to his wife*) Why should we wait every morning for a golden egg from our beautiful goose. If we cut the goose open, we will get all the golden eggs at once and we will be rich, rich, rich!

GOOSE I heard you, master! You wouldn't do that

84

to me would you? Remember, I'm your beautiful goose. Remember?

FARMER   I want all of your golden eggs now. NOW!

The farmer begins to chase the goose around the barnyard.

Now I have you and I will cut you open.

The farmer cuts the goose open.

Oh no! My beautiful goose is not full of golden eggs. Oh no! What have I done!

Moral   He who is too greedy may end up with nothing.

Suggestion for staging

Use the whole classroom for the goose chase, with much noise from the goose.

The farmer and his wife can moan and cry when they discover the goose is not full of golden eggs.

The Cat
and the Monkey

Characters   A Cat
A Monkey
The Owner of the House

Setting   It is a very cold day outside, and the
cat and monkey are sitting in front of
the fireplace.

MONKEY   The fire makes us feel so warm, and you
look so pretty sitting in front of the fireplace.
CAT   Thank you, Mr. Monkey.
MONKEY   Those chestnuts roasting in the fireplace
smell so good.
CAT   Yes, they certainly do, Mr. Monkey.

MONKEY I'm sure they taste so very good too. Wouldn't it be nice to eat some of them!

CAT Yes, it would, but how can we get them out of the fire?

MONKEY You are so clever at such things, you pretty cat. You are much more clever than I am!

CAT Oh thank you, Mr. Monkey.

MONKEY Why don't you pull some chestnuts out of the fire, and we will eat them!

CAT But I'm afraid of burning my delicate paws!

MONKEY Oh, but you are so nimble and quick. You won't burn your beautiful little graceful paw.

CAT Very well, I will pull out chestnuts for us to eat.

The cat begins to pull out chestnuts from the fire, but as quickly as she pulls them out the monkey eats them.

My paw is getting burned, and it hurts me!

MONKEY But you are doing very well! Keep trying!

OWNER Get away from the fireplace and stop eating my chestnuts. You both are very naughty.

The monkey and cat scamper to another part of the house.

CAT My paw is very burned, and I didn't even get one chestnut to eat! You ate them all, Mr. Monkey! Next time I'll know better, and I won't pull out any more chestnuts for you!

Moral Beware of people who flatter you, for they usually want something from you.

87

Suggestions for staging

The opening of a teacher desk makes an ideal fireplace; a wastepaper basket is a good place for the cat to quickly flip out chestnuts into the air for the monkey to catch.

The owner of the house should shout loudly.

The Dove
and the Ant

Characters　An Ant
　　　　　　A Dove
　　　　　　A Hunter

Setting　A meadow during a hot afternoon.

ANT　I'm so thirsty, I think I will go down to the
brook for a drink of cool water.
At the brook the ant accidentally falls in.
HELP! HELP! HELP! Someone save me!
HELP!

DOVE *(sitting in a nearby tree)*　Poor little ant, I feel
so sorry for him. What can I do to help? I know!
I'll drop a leaf into the brook which the ant can
use as a raft to get to shore.
*The dove drops the leaf into the brook, and the
ant is saved.*

ANT   Thank you, kind dove.

A hunter is creeping close to the tree.

HUNTER   (*whispering*)   Look at that beautiful dove in the tree. I'll spread my net and snare him.

ANT   Oh no you don't! That dove saved me from drowning, and I will not allow you to catch him in your net, Mr. Hunter.

The ant bites the hunter on the leg as hard as he can.

HUNTER   OUCH!

The dove is startled by the noise and swoops away to safety.

Moral   One good turn deserves another.

Suggestions for staging

The dove can perch on a classroom desk.

The brook can be a long piece of paper—any color.

The Wind
and the Sun

Characters   The Wind
The Sun
A Man

Setting   An open field.

WIND   Mr. Sun, you are so silly to say that you are
stronger and more powerful than I am.

SUN   But my dear Mr. Wind, you are stupid not to
realize that what I say is very true!

WIND   But my dear Mr. Sun, everybody, yes everybody, knows that I am stronger!

SUN   I don't believe what everybody says. People
are very often mistaken.

WIND   You really make me laugh the way you talk.

How could anyone or anything be stronger than the wind?

SUN   Yes, I agree that you are strong, but all I say is that you are not as strong as I am.

MAN   Will you two stop arguing. You are keeping me awake, and I have much work to do tomorrow.

WIND   It's all the sun's fault!

SUN   No it's not! It's all the wind's fault!

MAN   There you go again with your foolish argument. Tomorrow we will have a contest between you. I will wear my heavy cloak and the one that makes me take my cloak off will be the champion. Fair enough?

WIND   Yes.

SUN   Yes.

MAN   Good! Now go to sleep so I can rest, and we will meet in the open field tomorrow at noon. Good night.

The next day.

Are the two of you ready?

WIND   Yes.

SUN   Yes.

MAN   Good. I have on my heavy cloak. Mr. Wind, you will go first to see if you can make me take off my heavy cloak.

WIND   Get ready, sir, for soon you will be without a cloak.

The wind huffs and puffs and huffs and puffs, but the man wraps his cloak even more tightly around him.

Oh dear, I'm all out of breath! I'm all out of
wind, and I failed to remove the cloak.

MAN   All right, your turn, Mr. Sun.

SUN   I'm ready, sir.

*The sun begins to shine brightly upon the man,
and soon he feels so hot he removes his cloak.*

MAN   You win, Mr. Sun. You are the champion!

Moral   Kindness is more persuasive than force.

Suggestions for staging

When the wind huffs and puffs, the student
playing the man should do everything possible
to give the impression that the cloak is nearly
being blown off his back.

When the sun is sending out powerful rays, the
boy wearing the cloak should do everything possible to show how hot he is wearing it.

The wind could use a fan or just the air from
his mouth.

The sun could hold up a piece of bright yellow
paper to send out heat.

The Mouse
and the Frog

Characters A Little Mouse
 A Frog
 A Hawk

Setting In a woods early one spring morning.

LITTLE MOUSE What a beautiful spring morning! I
 think I'll go down to the pond to explore and
 see what is going on this bright early morning.
 The little mouse wanders down to the pond.

FROG Good morning, little mouse.

LITTLE MOUSE Good morning, Mr. Frog. Lovely
 morning.

FROG Have you come to visit my pond this lovely
 morning?

LITTLE MOUSE   Yes, I thought I would explore your pond this lovely spring morn.

FROG   Good! Come and let me show it to you.

LITTLE MOUSE   But I'm not a very good swimmer.

FROG   Have no fear for I will help you. Let me tie one of your legs to mine. Here is a reed that will serve just fine.

The frog ties the little mouse to his leg and then jumps into the pond and begins to swim to the bottom.

LITTLE MOUSE   HELP! HELP! HELP! Let me go, Mr. Frog, for I can't breathe! I will drown! HELP!

FROG   Sorry, my little mouse, but you are going to be a tasty breakfast for me!

The frog comes to the surface and begins to untie the drowned mouse from his leg.

HAWK   (*sitting way up high in a tree*)   That looks like a little mouse way down there that would make a tasty breakfast for me. I think I'll swoop down right now and grab him!

The hawk swoops down and grabs the little mouse. Of course the frog goes along also for he is still tied to the mouse.

FROG   HELP! HELP! HELP! HELP! HELP!

But the hawk does not pay the least bit of attention as he flies up to the sky.

Moral   He who plots to hurt others often hurts himself.

Suggestions for staging

When the frog is dragging the little mouse to the bottom of the pond, crawling underneath a large piece of cloth or underneath a table will convey the feeling of disappearing to the bottom of the pond.

When the hawk flies away with the mouse and the attached frog, running about the room will convey the idea of flying way up to the sky.

The Hare
and the Tortoise

Characters   A Hare
              A Tortoise
              A Fox

Setting   In a woods.

HARE   Ha-ha-ha-ha-ha-ha-ha-ha-ha-ha! My dear Mr.
   Tortoise, please forgive me for laughing, but
   I can't help it. Ha-ha-ha-ha-ha-ha-ha!

TORTOISE   What are you laughing at?

HARE   Ha-ha-ha-ha-ha-ha-ha! Your legs! Ha-ha-ha-
   ha-ha-ha!

TORTOISE   What is so funny about my legs?

HARE   They are so short! Ha-ha-ha-ha-ha-ha-ha! And you travel so slowly! You are truly a funny sight! Ha-ha-ha-ha-ha-ha!

TORTOISE   I'm glad you are so amused, but let me tell you this. Even though you be as swift as the wind, I will beat you in a race.

HARE   What did you say?

TORTOISE   I said I can beat you in a race!

HARE   HA-HA-HA-HA-HA-HA-HA-HA-HA!

TORTOISE   Are you afraid to accept my challenge?

HARE   Afraid? Ha-ha-ha-ha-ha-ha! You truly are a silly fool. You are so slow and I am so fast . . . how could you possibly win?

TORTOISE   We will never know unless we try it.

HARE   Ha-ha-ha-ha-ha-ha!

TORTOISE   Why don't you stop laughing so we can begin the race.

HARE   Ha-ha-ha-ha-ha! All right, I accept your challenge. Now, who will decide what course we run?

TORTOISE   Perhaps Mr. Fox over there will plan the course for us? Mr. Fox!

FOX   What can I do for you?

HARE   This silly tortoise has challenged me to run a race. Will you decide what course we are to run?

FOX   Certainly, glad to be of help. The course you will run will be the road that leads directly up the mountain, and the one who reaches the peak first is the winner.

TORTOISE   Fair enough.

HARE   I'm ready, Mr. Tortoise, are you? Ha-ha-ha-ha-ha-ha!

TORTOISE   Yes, I'm ready, Mr. Hare.

FOX   Get ready! On your mark! Get set! GO!
The race begins. The hare quickly runs far ahead, and the tortoise is left way behind.

HARE   This is a silly, silly race. I'm so far ahead I can't even see poor Mr. Tortoise. I think I'll take a little nap in this cool grass.
The hare falls sound asleep. The tortoise continues at his slow pace, quietly goes by the hare, and reaches the peak of the mountain first.
Well, that was a nice nap. I still don't see that silly tortoise. Ha-ha-ha-ha-ha-ha-ha-ha-ha-ha! Well, might as well go to the peak of the mountain and wait for him there. Ha-ha-ha-ha-ha-ha!
The hare strolls leisurely to the peak of the mountain where he finds the tortoise waiting.

TORTOISE   Hello, Mr. Hare! Where have you been? You see, I told you I could beat you in a race and I have!

Moral   Persistence pays.

Suggestions for staging
Circle the whole room as the race track.
A chair on top of a table can represent the mountain peak.
Much laughter from the hare—good loud laughter.

The City Mouse
and the Country Mouse

Characters   A City Mouse
A Country Mouse
A Huge Dog

Setting   The home of the country mouse.

COUNTRY MOUSE   My dear cousin from the city, how nice of you to come all this way to visit me.

CITY MOUSE   I'm glad to be here, although I will admit it was a long journey.

COUNTRY MOUSE   Please make yourself at home while I prepare dinner.

CITY MOUSE   Thank you, my country cousin.

COUNTRY MOUSE   Let's have our dinner outside un-
    derneath the big tree. The air smells so good,
    and we can relax. Is that all right with you?

CITY MOUSE   Anything you say cousin.

    *They carry the food outside and sit under a big
    tree.*

    Now, here is what we shall have to eat. Some
    bread, some cheese, some bacon, some beans,
    and for dessert we will go searching for some
    acorns.

CITY MOUSE   Thank you, country cousin, but how
    can you put up with such poor food as this?

COUNTRY MOUSE   Don't you like it? I think it's deli-
    cious!

CITY MOUSE   But the bread is moldy, and the cheese
    is hard, and the bacon and beans are dry!

COUNTRY MOUSE   I'm sorry you don't like it, but
    that's all I have to offer.

CITY MOUSE   I have a wonderful idea! Why don't
    you come to the city with me? There we can
    eat all kinds of delicious food, and for dessert
    we can have some very sweet cookies.

COUNTRY MOUSE   Very well, I will go to the city
    with you.

    The two mice begin their long trip to the city.

CITY MOUSE   Here we are! Look! The people who
    live here have not cleared the table and have
    left much food. Look at all the things we can
    eat!

COUNTRY MOUSE   I don't believe what I see! Is it all
    real? All this food!

CITY MOUSE   Yes, it's all real, and I eat this way every night. Try some of the sweet grapes, and the soft cheese, and the nuts, and the pudding, and the crackers. And for dessert we can eat the sweet tasty jelly.

COUNTRY MOUSE   You are right, my city cousin, your food is much better.

In another room the huge dog starts barking.
What was that?

CITY MOUSE   Hurry! Hurry! We have to leave quickly for that noise means danger!

The two mice scamper off the table and hide in a little hole in the wall. The dog enters barking. He sniffs at the hole but finally goes away.
I think it's safe to go back and finish our dinner.

COUNTRY MOUSE   No thank you, my city cousin.

CITY MOUSE   What are you doing?

COUNTRY MOUSE   I'm preparing to go back to my country home.

CITY MOUSE   You mean right now, with all that food still left on the table?

COUNTRY MOUSE   I'm leaving right now . . . this very minute!

CITY MOUSE   But I don't understand!

COUNTRY MOUSE   Let me explain, dear city cousin. Yes, I agree your food is much better and tastier than mine, but I don't enjoy eating always wondering when that dog is going to hear us and rush in. Good-bye dear city cousin. I'm going back to the peace and quiet of the country where I won't have to worry about dogs. Good-bye.

Moral   Better dry bread and moldy cheese in peace than sweet cookies and tasty pudding in fear.

Suggestions for staging
Encourage the students to use the whole room when traveling from country to city.
The dog should be very bold and loud.
Encourage the mice to tremble in their hole.
A large table can serve as the dining table with all the goodies.
Encourage the mice to explore the table in detail.

The Donkey, the Rooster, and the Lion

Characters   A Donkey
             A Rooster
             A Lion

Setting   The outskirts of a barnyard late one night.

LION   I think everyone is asleep in the barnyard. Now is my chance to jump on that delicious donkey and eat him up. I am very hungry! I will creep up very slowly so as not to awaken him, and then I will have a delicious dinner for myself. I must move quietly though.

The lion carefully opens the barnyard gate and very slowly creeps up to the sleeping donkey and gets set to pounce upon him.

ROOSTER   Cock-a-doodle-do!   Cock-a-doodle-do!
COCK-A-DOODLE-DO!
The lion is so startled that he runs back into the forest.

DONKEY   Thank you, Mr. Rooster, for making such a noise. You really scared off that dangerous lion.

ROOSTER   I was glad to be of help.

DONKEY   You mean to say that all you did was crow, and you frightened away that dangerous lion?

ROOSTER   Yes, that's all I did.

DONKEY   Well, if that lion was scared away so easily, then I'll go after him and really scare him with a good hard kick!

ROOSTER   I think the noise I made surprised him. That's why he ran away.

DONKEY   Even so, I will go after him and really hurt him. I'm sick and tired of that lion hanging around outside our barnyard. He needs to be taught a lesson. If he is frighened by your crow, he's really just a big scaredy-cat. I'm just the one to give him a good hard kick so he'll go away.
The donkey chases after the lion, and the lion stops running and eats up the donkey.

Moral   False confidence and pride can lead to ruin.

Suggestions for staging

The rooster should crow very loudly as the donkey snores.

The lion should be hiding, ready to pounce upon the donkey.

Encourage the donkey to use the whole room when chasing the lion.

The Miser

Characters   A Miser
A Workman
A Neighbor

Setting   The home of a miser on the outskirts of town.

MISER   I have sold all my furniture, my dishes, and my clothes for this beautiful, beautiful, beautiful lump of gold! Look how it shines! Isn't it magnificent? Yes, and it's all mine! All my very own! . . . Now comes my problem. Where shall I hide my beautiful lump of gold? Where? Where? Where? Let me think. . . . Yes, I'll bury it in my backyard.
The miser digs a deep, deep hole and buries his lump of gold in the middle of the night so no will see him.

The next day.

Is my gold safe? I had better check to see if it is still safe. Suppose someone has stolen it. . . . Oh, I'm so worried! (*He digs up the gold.*) Thank heavens it is safe! Now to bury it again. I don't think anyone saw me. I'm sure no one saw me.

The miser goes back into his house.

WORKMAN   I wonder why that old miser keeps digging a hole in his backyard and then covering it up? I'm very curious. I think I'll check to see what is buried in that hole.

The workman digs up the hole and discovers the lump of gold.

Why it's a lump of gold! I think I'll keep it!

The workman runs away with the lump of gold.

MISER   I had better check my lump of gold to see if it is safe. Oh no! Oh no! Oh no! My lump of gold is gone! Help! Help! Help! Someone has stolen my lump of gold! HELP! HELP!

NEIGHBOR   Why are you crying so?

MISER   Someone has stolen my lump of gold. It's gone! Gone! Gone! Do you hear me . . . it's gone! GONE! GONE!

NEIGHBOR   Don't be so unhappy.

MISER   Are you crazy to say that? My lump of gold is gone, and you say don't be so unhappy!

NEIGHBOR   No, I'm not crazy and I'll tell you why. Place a stone in the hole and pretend it is your precious lump of gold.

MISER   You don't make sense!

NEIGHBOR   I make great sense. The stone will fur-
nish you the same service as your lump of gold,
for you do not make much use of your gold but
bury it in the ground. So, pretend a lump of
stone is your lump of gold.

Moral   Money has no value if it is not used.

Suggestions for staging
The miser can cry and groan loudly.
Encourage strenuous digging and burying.
The workman can sneak away.

The Gnat
and the Lion

Characters A Gnat
A Lion
A Spider

Setting In the middle of a forest.

GNAT Well, well, well if it isn't Mr. Lion!

LION Get away from me, you silly little gnat. You are nothing but a nuisance!

GNAT I am not afraid of you, and I don't think you are stronger than I am!

LION Go away and let me get my rest.

GNAT All you can do is scratch with your claws and bite with your teeth. I repeat, I am stronger than you!

LION Are you still here? Go away!

GNAT Don't be so sure of yourself, Mr. Lion. Come,

I'll challenge you to a fight to prove to you that I am stronger than you.

LION   Very well! Anything to shut you up.

The gnat begins to buzz about the lion, stinging him on the nose, on his tail, in his ear, and on his head. The poor lion finally gives up trying to slap the gnat with his paw.

Yes, you win, you pesky little gnat!

GNAT   I told you so! I told you so!

The gnat buzzes about the forest feeling very proud and bragging to everyone how powerful he is.

Look at me everyone! The lion thought he was the king of the forest, but I showed him up! Yes, he may be bigger than I am and have sharper claws, but I defeated him. He admitted himself that I won the fight. What a powerful fellow I am! I'm stronger than the lion!

The gnat runs into a spider's web and is trapped.

SPIDER   Well, well, well, well, my little gnat. I have you trapped in my web.

GNAT   HELP! HELP! HELP!

SPIDER   No one hears you my little gnat, and the more you struggle the more you are trapped!

GNAT   Poor me! How is it that I can defeat the powerful lion, but I am helpless against a weak spider? Poor me!

SPIDER   And now, my little gnat, I am going to have a delicious meal by eating you up!

The spider gobbles up the little gnat.

Moral　There is always someone or something stronger than you.

Suggestions for staging
The gnat should be encouraged to really buzz about the room.
The lion can do much howling and much slapping as the gnat stings.
The spider's web can be a large cobweb drawn on the blackboard; when the gnat leans against it he is trapped.

The Lion, the Fox, and the Donkey

Characters A Lion
A Fox
A Donkey

Setting In the middle of a forest.

LION   Instead of each of us hunting by ourselves, Mr. Fox and Mr. Donkey, why don't we hunt together. In this way we will be sure of catching something good to eat for our dinner.

FOX   Say, that's a very good idea, Mr. Lion.

DONKEY   Yes, I'll go along with that idea.

LION   Fine! Let us begin our hunt.
The three of them start off on their hunt and catch a tasty deer.

FOX   Yes, that certainly was a great idea of yours to hunt together. This deer will make a tasty dinner!

DONKEY   Well now, let me divide the deer into three parts . . . one part for each of us as we agreed in our plan.

The donkey divides the deer into three equal parts.

FOX   Very well divided into equal parts, Mr. Donkey.

DONKEY   Thank you, Mr. Fox. Now, who will make the first choice of the part they want?

LION   I will, Mr. Donkey, and the part I want is YOU!

The lion jumps upon the donkey and devours him.

Now, Mr. Fox, you divide the deer and decide how much is for me and how much is for you.

FOX   Certainly, Mr. Lion. The first part of the deer is for you, and this second part of the deer is for you, and this third part of the deer is for you.

LION   Very well done, Mr. Fox. Who taught you how to divide things so well?

FOX   I learned it from the donkey by seeing what happened to him!

Moral   Happy is the person who learns from the misfortune of others.

Suggestions for staging
Use the whole room for the hunt.
The deer can be a cardboard box that can be divided into three parts.
When the lion pounces upon the donkey, encourage much noise and activity.

114

The Crab
and the Fox

Characters   First Crab
             Second Crab
             A Fox

Setting   Near the seashore.

FIRST CRAB   I'm tired of living near and in the water.
I'm always so damp and cold. Let's move somewhere else.

SECOND CRAB   Where do you have in mind, cousin
crab?

FIRST CRAB   The meadow looks like a nice place to
live. It looks so green and smells so good.

SECOND CRAB   But don't you think that would be a
dangerous place for us to live?

FIRST CRAB   Don't be so frightened of everything.
Why couldn't we live there?

SECOND CRAB   Something tells me that it's best that we stay near the water.

FIRST CRAB   I don't care what you say, my dear cousin. I'm moving to the beautiful fresh meadow.

SECOND CRAB   Good luck, cousin, but I'm staying where I belong.

The first crab slowly makes his way to the meadow.

FIRST CRAB   Oh, it smells so good! I'm so glad I left my watery home, so very glad!

FOX   Well, well, well . . . what do we have here in the meadow?

FIRST CRAB   Mr. Fox, you aren't going to harm me are you?

FOX   I'm going to eat you up for my dinner, little crab!

FIRST CRAB   Boo-hoo! Boo-hoo! Why did I ever leave my seashore home? Boo-hoo! Boo-hoo! Yes, I deserve this fate!

The fox gobbles up the little crab.

Moral   It pays to be content with your lot.

Suggestions for staging
The first crab should move slowly from the seashore to the meadow.
The little crab can cry loudly as the fox prepares to eat him up.

Plays for Four Students

The Mother Lark
and Her Babies

Characters   Mother Lark
                First baby Lark
                Second baby Lark
                A Farmer

Setting   A nest in the middle of a wheat field
             early one morning.

MOTHER LARK   Children, I am going to catch some
worms for our breakfast. While I am gone, you
stay in the nest and listen carefully.

FIRST BABY LARK   What should we listen for,
Mother?

MOTHER LARK   Listen and see if you can find out when the wheat field is going to be cut for we will have to move our nest before that happens.

SECOND BABY LARK   We will listen carefully, Mother.

Mother lark flies away. Farmer enters.

FARMER   I think I will ask my neighbors to help me cut the wheat field today.

FIRST BABY LARK   Did you hear that?

SECOND BABY LARK   Yes, I heard.

Mother lark flies back.

MOTHER LARK   Well, what did you hear my little ones?

FIRST BABY LARK   Oh Mother, Mother, the farmer is asking his neighbors to help him cut the wheat field today . . . this very day!

SECOND BABY LARK   We had better move our nest now, Mother!

MOTHER LARK   Don't be alarmed, my little ones. There is no need to move our nest today. Now, open your mouths for here are the worms I promised to find for you.

FIRST BABY LARK   Thank you, Mother.

SECOND BABY LARK   Thank you, Mother.

The next day.

MOTHER LARK   I am going to catch some worms for your breakfast. While I am gone, listen carefully.

FIRST BABY LARK   We will listen carefully, Mother.

SECOND BABY LARK   We will listen very carefully, Mother.

Mother lark flies away. Farmer enters.

FARMER   I think I will ask my friends to help me cut my wheat field today.

FIRST BABY LARK   Did you hear that?

SECOND BABY LARK   Yes, I heard it!

Mother lark flies back.

MOTHER LARK   What did you hear, my little ones?

FIRST BABY LARK   Oh Mother, let us hurry away now!

SECOND BABY LARK   Yes Mother, let us hurry away for the farmer is asking his friends to help him cut the wheat field today!

MOTHER LARK   No need to worry, my little ones, for the wheat field won't be cut today. Open your mouths for here are the worms I promised you.

FIRST BABY LARK   Thank you, Mother.

SECOND BABY LARK   Thank you, Mother.

The third day.

MOTHER LARK   I am going to catch some worms for your breakfast. Listen carefully while I am gone.

FIRST BABY LARK   We will listen carefully, Mother.

SECOND BABY LARK   We will listen very carefully, Mother.

Mother lark flies away. Farmer enters.

FARMER   I think I will cut the wheat myself today.

FIRST BABY LARK   Did you hear what I heard?

SECOND BABY LARK   I certainly did hear what you heard!

Mother lark flies back.

MOTHER LARK   Well, what did you hear today, my little ones?

FIRST BABY LARK   Let us hurry and move our nest.

SECOND BABY LARK   Yes, Mother, let us hurry and move our nest for we heard the farmer say he is going to cut the wheat field himself today.

MOTHER LARK   Yes, my little ones, we must hurry and move our nest for today the wheat field surely will be cut. When a man does not depend on anyone to help him, the job will get done.

Moral   Self-help is the best help.

Suggestions for staging
The nest could be under a table.
When the mother bird searches for worms, she should fly about the room.

Peacock and Juno

Characters   A Peacock
The goddess Juno
A Nightingale
An Owl

Setting   Near a forest.

OWL   Sing us another pretty song, Miss Nightingale,
for you have such a lovely voice.
NIGHTINGALE   Thank you for the compliment, Mr.
Owl.
Nightingale bursts into song.
OWL   Yes, you truly have a most delicate voice.
Thank you, Miss Nightingale, for making all

the creatures of the forest so happy with your song.

PEACOCK I, too, have a nice singing voice!

The peacock attempts to sing but all he makes are ugly, harsh sounds.

OWL Ha-ha-ha-ha-ha-ha-ha-ha-ha-ha! When you sing, you are the laughing stock of the forest, Mr. Peacock. I suggest that you never attempt to sing again. I think it best that you parade about and show everyone your beautiful plumage.

He flies away.

PEACOCK Why don't I have a beautiful voice? I, too, would love to make all the creatures of the forest happy with my voice. I'm so unhappy that I can't sing!

JUNO Don't be so unhappy, Mr. Peacock. It is true that you can't sing like Miss Nightingale, but you are far more beautiful. Your feathers are the talk of the forest.

PEACOCK But what good is my beauty if I can't sing?

He begins to cry.

Boo-hoo-hoo. Boo-hoo-hoo.

JUNO There, there . . . don't cry, Mr. Peacock, for it was decided a long time ago that each creature of the forest would be noted for certain things. For example, the nightingale would be famous for her song, the eagle for his strength, and you, Mr. Peacock, for your beauty. Now, let me see you spread your wings and walk proudly.

PEACOCK Oh very well, I'll strut about and show

my plumage to all the creatures of the forest.
He proudly struts about.

Moral   Each person has his strong point.

Suggestions for staging
When the nightingale sings, the student can whistle, hum, or sing.
When the peacock sings, his sounds should be very harsh and ugly.
When the peacock struts, he should use the whole room and truly strut.
The goddess Juno could be just a voice or appear in person.

The Doe
and the Lion

Characters A Doe
              A Lion
              First Hunter
              Second Hunter

Setting In a forest near the cave of a lion.

FIRST HUNTER Look! I see a doe! Get your rifle ready!

SECOND HUNTER Where? Where? I don't see a doe!

FIRST HUNTER Stop making so much noise! Look . . . there between the branches. See it now?

SECOND HUNTER Yes! It's a beautiful doe!

DOE I smell danger! Where shall I run? There's only one place to hide and that's in the nearby cave.

The doe runs into the cave.

LION Now I have you, my little doe.

DOE Oh dear, what have I done? What have I done!

LION You made a very foolish decision running into my cave.

DOE But the two hunters were after me, and I had to hide somewhere. Please do not eat me up!

LION Sorry, my friend!

The lion gobbles up the doe.

Moral In avoiding one evil, care must be taken not to fall into another.

Suggestions for staging

Make use of the whole classroom. The hunters can be at one end of the room when they spot the doe at the other end.

The lion's den can be under a table.

The Dogs
and the Hides

Characters   Black Dog
White Dog
Brown Dog
Spotted Dog

Setting   Near a big river.

BLACK DOG   See those big poles sticking out of the middle of the river?

WHITE DOG   Yes, I see them. What are they?

BLACK DOG   They are poles, and attached to those poles are some delicious hides!

BROWN DOG   That makes me extra hungry! Let's go and get them.

SPOTTED DOG   Don't be silly. How can we get them when the water in the middle of the river is deep and swift?

BROWN DOG   What shall we do then? I'm very hungry!

WHITE DOG   I am very hungry too!

BLACK DOG   I know how we can get to the hides.

SPOTTED DOG   Tell us! Tell us!

WHITE DOG   Hurry and tell us!

BROWN DOG   Yes, hurry, for I'm starving!

BLACK DOG   We can drink up all the water in the river.

SPOTTED DOG   That's a wonderful idea!

WHITE DOG   Do you really think we can drink up all the water? There's a great deal of water in that river.

BLACK DOG   Of course we can drink up all the water in the river if we all work together. Now let's get started.

The four dogs start drinking and drinking and drinking.

WHITE DOG   Oh dear . . . oh dear! I'm so full of water I'm going to float away!

The white dog floats down the river out of sight.

SPOTTED DOG   Look! Look! The white dog is floating away!

BLACK DOG   Don't worry about him. That just means there will be more of the hides for us.

BROWN DOG   Oh dear . . . oh dear! I'm so full of water I'm going to float away!

The brown dog floats down the river out of sight.

SPOTTED DOG   Look! Look! The brown dog is floating away!

BLACK DOG   Don't worry about him. That just leaves the two of us to split the hides, and that means more for both of us!

SPOTTED DOG   Oh dear! Oh dear! I'm so full of water that I'm going to float away too! Help me! Help me! HELP! HELP! HELP!

BLACK DOG   I'm not going to help you for now the hides are all for me!

The spotted dog floats away out of sight.

I must now finish drinking the water in the river and then I will be able to eat the delicious hides all by myself. (*He drinks and drinks and drinks.*) I'm almost finished. Just a few more gallons and then I'll eat the hides . . . the delicious hides! I can hardly wait!

The black dog drinks and drinks and finally becomes so full of water that he bursts!

Moral   Do not attempt the impossible.

Suggestions for staging
A large piece of cloth or a blanket can be the river.

As each dog floats away, a member of the audience can drag the blanket along the floor to indicate the dog floating away.

As each dog floats down the river, he can yell for help.

There should be a loud explosive sound when the black dog bursts.

The Mother
and the Wolf

Characters   A Mother
               A Baby
               A Wolf
               The Wolf's Wife

Setting   A cottage in a forest.

WOLF   I hear a baby crying! I'll go and see what it's all about.
The wolf creeps to the cottage. Coming close to the cottage window, he sees a mother holding her young baby.

BABY   WAH! WAH! WAH! WAH! WAH!

MOTHER   Stop your crying and fall asleep. It's way past your bedtime.

BABY   WAH! WAH! WAH! WAH! WAH!

MOTHER   Stop your crying I say!

BABY   WAH! WAH! WAH! WAH! WAH!

MOTHER   If you don't stop your crying, I will throw you out the window and a wolf will eat you up!

WOLF   I'm going to wait right outside this window so I'll be ready to catch the baby when the mother throws him out the window.

BABY   WAH! WAH! WAH! WAH! WAH!

The wolf waits and waits and waits but nothing happens.

WOLF   It is getting dark and it's cold. I guess the mother is not going to throw the baby out the window after all.

BABY   WAH! WAH! WAH! WAH! WAH!

WOLF   I have been waiting for hours and hours. I'm tired and I'm going home!

The wolf heads for his home.

WOLF'S WIFE   Where have you been so long? You have been gone for hours!

WOLF   I was waiting for our dinner outside a cottage window.

WOLF'S WIFE   What made you think you were going to get our dinner from a cottage window?

WOLF   I heard a mother tell her baby that if he didn't stop crying she was going to throw him out of the window.

132

WOLF'S WIFE   You silly fool. And you waited hours
for that? Do you honestly think a mother would
throw her baby out of a window? You truly are
a stupid wolf!

Moral   Don't believe everything you hear.

Suggestions for staging
The baby should cry loudly and clearly.
Mother and child could be sitting on a chair on
a table while the wolf on the floor looks up to
the cottage window.

The Ox
and the Frog

Characters   First Little Frog
                      Second Little Frog
                      Third Little Frog
                      The Mother Frog

Setting   A little pond in the middle of the woods. On three rocks in the center of the pond sit three little frogs.

FIRST LITTLE FROG   Oh Mother! Oh Mother!
SECOND LITTLE FROG   Mother, where are you!
THIRD LITTLE FROG   Mother, come quickly!

MOTHER FROG   Coming children.

FIRST LITTLE FROG   Hurry, Mother! Hurry!

MOTHER FROG   Now, what is all this excitement about?

FIRST LITTLE FROG   We have just seen a most frightening monster!

SECOND LITTLE FROG   He was as big as a tall, tall tree!

THIRD LITTLE FROG   And he had a long, long tail, and he had long pointed horns!

MOTHER FROG   There is no reason to be frightened, my children. That was just Mr. Ox. Yes, he was big, but not much bigger than I am. Now you watch children. I'm going to huff and puff and make myself as big as Mr. Ox. (*She huffs and puffs to make herself as big as Mr. Ox.*) Now, children, am I just as big as Mr. Ox?

FIRST LITTLE FROG   Oh no, Mother!

SECOND LITTLE FROG   Oh no, Mother!

THIRD LITTLE FROG   Oh no, Mother! Mr. Ox was much, much bigger!

MOTHER FROG   Then I will try again. Now watch me children. (*She huffs and puffs and huffs and puffs.*) Now children, certainly I must be as big as Mr. Ox!

FIRST LITTLE FROG   Oh no, Mother!

SECOND LITTLE FROG   Oh no, Mother!

THIRD LITTLE FROG   Oh no, Mother. Mr. Ox was much, much bigger!

MOTHER FROG   Very well, I will try again. Now watch me, children.

The mother frog huffs and puffs and huffs and puffs and huffs and puffs and explodes.

Moral   A small man may destroy himself by trying to be bigger than he is.

Suggestions for staging
Chairs for the audience can be placed in a circle to suggest a pond in the middle.
The mother frog can get bigger and bigger by starting on the floor, then moving to a chair, and finally to a table where she explodes and falls to the floor.

The Goat
and the Donkey

Characters   A Goat
A Donkey
A Master
A Doctor

Setting   On a farm.

GOAT   I envy the donkey! I am very jealous of all the delicious food he is given while all I have is scraps and things I find for myself. Perhaps I can play a trick on him so there will be more food for me.
The donkey wanders by.
DONKEY   Hello, Mr. Goat. You seem to be very sad today. What is the matter?
GOAT   I was feeling very sorry for you.
DONKEY   Feeling sorry for me? Why? I'm very happy on this farm. My master treats me very well. Don't feel sorry for me, Mr. Goat.

GOAT   But I do! I do! The master is not treating you well at all! Look how hard he makes you work at the mill grinding corn!

DONKEY   I never thought of it that way.

GOAT   And, also, look at the heavy burdens he makes you carry each day back and forth from the mill.

DONKEY   Yes, you are right! I do work very hard. What do you suggest I do to make my life easier?

GOAT   I have a wonderful idea! Why don't you pretend to have a fainting spell and fall into the ditch. Then your master will have to give you a long rest.

DONKEY   That's a great idea! Thank you, Mr. Goat, thank you very much.

The donkey throws himself into a ditch and is hurt by his fall.

MASTER   Help! Help! Help! My wonderful donkey has fallen into the ditch! Help! Help! Someone come and help. HELP!

DOCTOR   I am a doctor. May I be of help?

MASTER   Oh yes, yes! Look! My wonderful donkey, my loyal donkey, has fallen into a ditch and seems to be close to death! What can I do to save him doctor?

DOCTOR   Let me think. Let me think. I think the best way to save your wonderful donkey is to pour the blood of a goat over his wounds. I'm sure that will help him recover.

MASTER   Thank you, doctor, thank you. I will do just that.

GOAT   Oh no! My idea has backfired! Oh no!

The goat hearing the words of the doctor begins to run away, but the master catches him and kills him. Then he pours the blood of the goat over the serious wounds of the donkey, and the donkey recovers.

MASTER   Now, my wonderful donkey, you are better, and I am so very, very happy. I am sorry about my goat, but I had to do something to save my wonderful, hard working donkey.

Moral   To envy others is foolish indeed.

Suggestions for staging
The goat and the donkey could be standing on a table from which the donkey jumps off into the ditch.
The master wails and cries when he discovers his donkey in the ditch.
The chase of the goat should make use of the whole area of the classroom.

The Wolf
and the Crane

Characters   A Wolf
A Crane
A Rabbit
A Donkey

Setting   In a woods one morning.

WOLF   Oh my, this is a delicious little lamb I am
eating. Yes, yes! Very, very tasty! Oh, it tastes so
good that I can't eat it fast enough.
*The wolf eats so fast that a bone sticks in his
throat.*
Ouch! Oh, that bone hurts my throat! I can't
get it out, and it's very painful! Ouch! What
shall I do! . . . I'll run down the road and perhaps I'll find someone that will help me. (*He
runs down the road.*) HELP! HELP! HELP!
I am choking! HELP! HELP! HELP!
RABBIT   What are you yelling about, Mr. Wolf?

WOLF Oh gentle rabbit, please stick you head in my throat and pull out the bone that is choking me. Please! Please!

RABBIT Not I, Mr. Wolf.

WOLF I'll give you much money if you will remove the bone.

RABBIT Not I, Mr. Wolf.

The rabbit scampers away.

WOLF Someone help me! I am choking! HELP! HELP! HELP!

DONKEY What are you yelling about, Mr. Wolf?

WOLF A bone in my throat is killing me! Please pull it out!

DONKEY Not I, Mr. Wolf.

WOLF But I will give you much money!

DONKEY Good-bye Mr. Wolf.

The donkey runs away.

WOLF HELP! HELP! HELP!

CRANE What is wrong, Mr. Wolf?

WOLF Oh Mr. Crane, you with your long beak could really help me. Please pull the bone out of my throat.

CRANE Well, I don't know if I should.

WOLF I'll give you a great deal of money if you will.

CRANE Very well, for a great deal of money I will do you the favor of pulling the stuck bone out of your throat.

The crane sticks his long beak down the wolf's throat and gently pulls out the bone.

There! Now where is the money you promised me?

WOLF   I promised you some money?

CRANE   Yes, you certainly did!

WOLF   Look, Mr. Crane, don't ask me for money. You were lucky to get your head out of my throat without it being snapped off by my sharp teeth. Consider yourself very lucky indeed, Mr. Crane.

Moral   Gratitude and greed do not go together.

Suggestions for staging
The wolf should run about feeling much pain in his throat.
The rabbit and the donkey dare not come too close to the wolf.
The crane could use his hand to remove the bone.

The Dogs
and the Fox

Characters   A Gray Dog
A White Dog
A Spotted Dog
A Fox

Setting   Near the forest where the dogs find the
skin of a lion.

GRAY DOG   Well, well, well, if it isn't the skin of a
lion.

WHITE DOG   Yes, it does look like the skin of a lion.

SPOTTED DOG   Let's attack it!

GRAY DOG   Great idea!

The three dogs attack the skin of the lion.

WHITE DOG   Look how brave I am!

SPOTTED DOG   Look how ferocious I am!

GRAY DOG   My sharp teeth are ripping the skin of
the lion!

WHITE DOG   Who dares say that we are afraid of a
lion!

SPOTTED DOG   Yes, lion, we are defeating you!

The three dogs chew the skin of the lion to bits.

GRAY DOG   Well, we certainly did a good job on that lion!

WHITE DOG   We certainly won that difficult battle!

SPOTTED DOG   We most certainly did!

FOX   What are you three doing?

GRAY DOG   Look, Mr. Fox, we just defeated a lion!

WHITE DOG   Yes, come and take a look!

SPOTTED DOG   It wasn't easy, but we won!

FOX   If the lion had been alive, you would have soon discovered that his claws are much stronger than all your teeth put together.

Moral   It is easy to kick a person when he is down.

Suggestions for staging
A piece of crepe paper can represent the skin of the lion; it can easily be stretched, pulled, and ripped by the dogs.
Encourage much noise from the dogs as they attack the lion skin.

Mercury
and the Workmen

Characters   Mercury, a god
First Workman
Second Workman
His Wife

Setting   In a forest near a deep pool.

FIRST WORKMAN   Poor me! Poor me! I just dropped my wooden-handled axe into the deep pool! How will I get it out? Poor me! How will I be able to chop trees so I can make money for food? What will I do now? Alas! Poor me! Poor me!

MERCURY   Why are you crying, wood chopper?

FIRST WORKMAN   Alas! Poor me! Poor me!

MERCURY   Stop your crying and wailing and tell me what is wrong. Perhaps I can help you.

FIRST WORKMAN   How can you possibly help me! I just dropped my axe into the deep pool by accident, and there is no way of getting it out! Oh poor, poor me!

MERCURY   Allow me to dive into the deep pool and see if I can find your wooden axe (*He dives into the pool and comes up holding a golden axe.*) Is this the axe you dropped into the deep pool by mistake?

FIRST WORKMAN   No, that's not mine. Mine was not a golden axe.

MERCURY   Let me try again. (*He dives into the deep pool for the second time and comes up with a silver axe.*) Is this the axe you accidentally dropped into the deep pool?

FIRST WORKMAN   No, that's not mine. Mine was not a silver axe.

MERCURY   Let me try again, wood chopper. (*He dives into the deep pool for the third time and comes up with an axe with a wooden handle.*) Is this the axe you dropped into the deep pool by accident?

FIRST WORKMAN   Oh yes, yes, yes! That is my axe! Thank you for finding it! Now I can chop down trees and earn money for food!

MERCURY   You are a very honest man, wood chopper, and to reward you for your honesty, I am

146

giving you the axe with the silver handle and the axe with the golden handle.

He suddenly disappears.

FIRST WORKMAN   I am rich! I am rich! I must rush home and tell my neighbor.

He rushes home.

SECOND WORKMAN   What are you so excited about?

FIRST WORKMAN   Listen! Listen! I dropped my wooden-handled axe into the deep pool by mistake, and a man not only found it for me, but also found an axe with a silver handle and an axe with a golden handle and gave them both to me. I am rich, rich, rich! I must now rush home to tell my wife.

He rushes away.

SECOND WORKMAN   How fortunate my friend is. I wish I could be as lucky.

HIS WIFE   Don't be so stupid! Why don't you go to the deep pool and throw in your axe and pretend it was an accident.

SECOND WORKMAN   That's a great idea! I'll do that now.

He rushes to the deep pool and throws in his axe.

Poor me! Poor me! I have just lost my axe in the deep pool. What shall I do? What shall I do?

MERCURY   Why are you crying?

SECOND WORKMAN   I just lost my axe in the deep pool. Will you find it for me? I know you can find it if you really try.

MERCURY   I will try, wood chopper.

He dives into the deep pool and comes up with a golden axe.

Is this your axe with a golden handle?

SECOND WORKMAN   Yes! Yes! Yes! That's my axe! That's the axe I lost!

MERCURY   LIAR! LIAR! LIAR! You are a liar! And for punishment I am throwing the axe back into the deep pool, and I will not get your wooden-handled axe for you!

Moral   Honesty is the best policy.

Suggestions for staging
The deep pool can be several desks placed in a circle for Mercury to jump into.
When Mercury vanishes, the second workman can sob loudly.

The Lion's Share

Characters   A Lion
A Fox
A Jackal
A Wolf

Setting   A very deep part of a forest.

LION   Listen, my good friends. The hunting is very poor this winter and almost every day we go hungry, right?

FOX   Very true, Mr. Lion.

JACKAL   I have caught nothing for two days.

WOLF   The same is true of my efforts.

LION   I have an excellent idea! Whenever one of us is lucky enough to catch something, we should divide it evenly with the rest. This way we will all have a bit of something to eat each day.

FOX   An excellent idea!

JACKAL   I agree to the plan.

WOLF   The idea sounds good to me.

LION   Then we are all in agreement?

FOX   Right!

JACKAL   Right!

WOLF   Right!

LION   Remember, then, let us be friends as well as neighbors. Let us share evenly. Now off to the hunt!

The animals scatter in four different directions.

FOX   Come here, everyone! Come here! I have caught a deer!

All the animals come running and gather around the fox and his prey.

LION   Very good, Mr. Fox!

JACKAL   Very good indeed, Mr. Fox!

WOLF   Well done, Mr. Fox!

FOX   Now let us begin to eat for I'm very, very, very hungry!

LION   Just a moment, neighbors. Remember our agreement! Remember there are four of us and we must divide evenly. Remember? I will now tear the deer into quarters.

The lion rips the deer into four equal parts.

JACKAL   Well done, Mr. Lion.

WOLF   Now let's eat for I too am very, very, very hungry!

LION   Just a moment!

FOX   What's the problem, Mr. Lion? Why should we wait?

LION I will explain. Now this quarter is mine as we agreed. Now this second quarter is also mine because I am a lion. Now this third quarter is also mine for I am stronger than all of you. And this last quarter is also mine, and if any of you dare touch it, you will not leave this place alive! Any questions?

FOX No questions, Mr. Lion.

JACKAL No questions, Mr. Lion.

WOLF No questions from me, Mr. Lion.

LION Very good thinking on your parts. Yes indeed, very good thinking!

The lion proceeds to eat the complete deer as the other animals watch.

Moral The law of the mighty is might makes right.

Suggestions for staging
When searching for food, the animals should explore the entire classroom.
A cardboard box can be the deer.
When eating the deer, the lion should show his great enjoyment with munching sounds and smacking his lips.

The Fox
and the Old Lion

Characters   An Old Lion
A Fox
A Rabbit
A Jackal

Setting   The opening of a cave deep in a forest.

OLD LION   I have grown so old that I am no longer able to hunt for food. But even though I am old, I still get hungry and I need something to eat. What am I to do? I know what I will do

. . . I'll pretend I'm very ill, and when visitors enter my cave to visit me, I'll eat them up!

He goes deep into his cave and begins to groan and moan.

Oh I feel so sick . . . so very sick! Someone come and help a poor old sick lion!

RABBIT   Are you all right in there, Mr. Lion?

OLD LION   No, little rabbit. I am very sick! Why don't you enter my cave and visit for a while.

RABBIT   Yes, I will visit with you for a while, Mr. Lion. You do sound extremely ill!

He enters the cave, and the old lion eats him up.

OLD LION   Oh, I feel so very ill . . . so very, very ill. Someone come and help a poor old sick lion!

JACKAL   You sound very ill, Mr. Lion. Is there anything I can do to help you feel better?

OLD LION   Oh yes, little jackal. Come into my cave and visit for a while. I know that will cheer me up.

JACKAL   Yes, I have time to visit for a short while.

He enters the cave, and the old lion eats him up.

OLD LION   Oh poor me . . . poor me! I'm an old sick lion and so very, very, very, ill!

FOX   You don't sound too well today, Mr. Lion.

OLD LION   How true! How true! I feel so ill! Also I am very lonely . . . so very lonely! Won't you come into my cave and visit for a short while? It certainly would cheer me up.

FOX   I don't know if I should, Mr. Lion.

OLD LION   Why do you speak that way? Why do you hesitate?

FOX I really don't think I should enter your cave at all!

OLD LION Why? Why?

FOX Well, it seems that you have had numerous visitors already by all these tracks in front of your cave, but all the tracks go only one way. I'll visit you when all the animals who have already visited you come out. Good-bye, Mr. Lion. Hope you feel better real soon!

Moral Be warned by what happens to others.

Suggestions for staging

The opening of the cave can be two or three desks pushed together so the lion can be out of sight. A closet or underneath an easel could also be a cave.

After each animal enters the cave, there should be much noise as the lion eats him up.

The Shepherd Boy
and the Wolf

Characters   A Boy
A Wolf
First Neighbor
Second Neighbor

Setting   A pasture near a village.

BOY   I'm so bored watching these sheep. I think I
will play a joke on the people of the village.
I will pretend a wolf is attacking the sheep, and
they will all come running and the joke will be
on them. I will yell good and loud so they will

hear me. . . . HELP! HELP! HELP! HELP! A wolf is eating the sheep! HELP! HELP! Come help me chase the wolf away!

FIRST NEIGHBOR I'm coming! I'm coming! Don't be frightened! I'm coming! . . . Where is the wolf? I don't see a wolf!

BOY Ha-ha-ha-ha-ha-ha-ha-ha! It was a joke! Ha-ha-ha-ha-ha-ha-ha!

FIRST NEIGHBOR I don't think it was such a funny joke! I ran all the way from the village to help you. No, it was not a very funny joke! You are a foolish boy. Now I must get back to my work which you so foolishly made me leave.
He returns to the village.

BOY Ha-ha-ha-ha-ha-ha-ha! I certainly fooled him! I think I will try the same joke again. . . . HELP! HELP! HELP! HELP! A wolf is eating the sheep! Come quickly!

SECOND NEIGHBOR I'm coming! I'm coming as fast as I can! Don't be frightened for I'm coming! . . . I don't see a wolf. Are you sure you saw a wolf?

BOY Ha-ha-ha-ha-ha-ha-ha-ha! It was a joke! Ha-ha-ha-ha-ha-ha!

SECOND NEIGHBOR I don't think it was such a funny joke! You should have better sense than to play such a joke on your neighbors and waste their valuable time!

BOY Ha-ha-ha-ha-ha-ha-ha-ha!

SECOND NEIGHBOR You are a silly boy and should be spanked!

He returns to the village.

BOY   Ha-ha-ha-ha-ha-ha-ha! It's so funny to see them come running. . . . What's that noise?

A huge wolf appears.

It's a wolf! He's going to eat my sheep! HELP! HELP! HELP! A WOLF IS EATING THE SHEEP! HELP! HELP! PLEASE HELP!

FIRST NEIGHBOR (*from the distance*)   I don't believe you.

SECOND NEIGHBOR (*from the distance*)   I don't believe you either.

BOY   I'm telling the truth! HELP! PLEASE HELP!

FIRST NEIGHBOR   You can't fool me again!

SECOND NEIGHBOR   You can't fool me again either!

The wolf gobbles up all the sheep.

Moral   No one believes a liar even when he is telling the truth.

Suggestions for staging

The boy should yell loudly as he calls for help and then laugh and laugh and laugh.

The neighbors should use the whole area of the classroom when running to help the boy.

The wolf should growl and snarl as he eats the imaginary sheep.

Plays for Five Students

The Meeting of the Mice

Characters First Mouse
Second Mouse
Third Mouse
A Very Young Mouse
A Very Old Mouse

Setting Midnight in the cellar of a house.

FIRST MOUSE What are we going to do? Oh, what are we going to do?

SECOND MOUSE It is a terrible situation! Yes, a terrible situation!

THIRD MOUSE Something has to be done about that horrible cat . . . and soon!

FIRST MOUSE Yesterday he caught and ate my cousin!

SECOND MOUSE My best friend just barely escaped from that cat this morning!

THIRD MOUSE I'm so afraid of leaving my little hole!

FIRST MOUSE I'm very much afraid too!

SECOND MOUSE Me too!

OLD MOUSE Everytime I want to go out for a walk, that terrible cat shows up.

THIRD MOUSE Well, what are we going to do about this situation?

FIRST MOUSE I don't know. I simply don't know!

SECOND MOUSE I don't know either. Boo-hoo! Boo-hoo!

THIRD MOUSE Stop crying! Your crying won't help at all!

FIRST MOUSE I know! Let's call a special meeting of all the mice in the house. Maybe someone will have an idea about what to do about that mean old cat!

SECOND MOUSE Good idea!

THIRD MOUSE Yes! A very good idea!

OLD MOUSE Maybe if we put our heads together, we can think of a way to solve this problem. That cat is becoming more dangerous everyday.

FIRST MOUSE Listen everybody! Listen to this announcement! Everyone come out of your holes for a special meeting.

SECOND MOUSE Special meeting for all mice who live in this house!

THIRD MOUSE   Hurry! Hurry! Special meeting of all mice. NOW!

All the mice gather for the special meeting

FIRST MOUSE   Is everyone here?

ALL   YES!

FIRST MOUSE   I have called a special meeting of all the mice to see if we can figure out how to stop the cat from catching us. Does anyone have any ideas?

SECOND MOUSE   I don't

THIRD MOUSE   I don't.

OLD MOUSE   I don't have any idea either.

YOUNG MOUSE   I have an excellent idea! I know how we can stop the cat from catching us.

FIRST MOUSE   Tell us! Tell us!

SECOND MOUSE   Hurry and tell us!

THIRD MOUSE   Speak up!

OLD MOUSE   Let's hear your brilliant idea, young mouse.

YOUNG MOUSE   My idea is to tie a bell around the cat's neck. The bell will warn us that she is coming and we can scamper away.

FIRST MOUSE   That is a wonderful idea!

SECOND MOUSE   An excellent idea!

THIRD MOUSE   Why didn't we think of that before!

OLD MOUSE   Yes, young mouse, that is a fine idea, but there is only one problem. Who will volunteer to tie the bell around the neck of the cat?

FIRST MOUSE   Not I!

SECOND MOUSE   Not I!

THIRD MOUSE   Not I!

OLD MOUSE   Not I!

YOUNG MOUSE   And not I, either!

All the mice return to their holes.

Moral   Foolish plans very seldom work.

Suggestions for staging

A corner of the classroom can be the meeting place.

Ask for student volunteers to be the extra mice at the special meeting.

The Farmer
and the Stork

Characters   A Farmer
A Stork
First Crane
Second Crane
Third Crane

Setting   A cornfield.

FARMER   I am sick and tired of those cranes that come to eat the seeds I plant every spring. This year I'm going to place a net to capture them. *He spreads a net and then hides in the bushes to await the arrival of the cranes.*

I must be very quiet for I see four cranes flying this way. Yes, I must be quiet . . . very, very, very quiet so I won't frighten them away. And I must also be ready to spring my net to catch them all.

The four birds come closer and closer and finally land on the field. The farmer springs the net and snares them.

FIRST CRANE   Help! I'm trapped! HELP!

SECOND CRANE   Help! I'm trapped! Help!

THIRD CRANE   Both my feet are trapped! Help!

STORK   Help! My leg is broken! Help! Please let me go, Mr. Farmer. Have pity on my broken leg!

FARMER   Why should I let you go? Every year you cranes eat the seeds I plant. When harvest time comes, I have no corn, and my family and I go hungry through the winter. I must stop you cranes from eating my seeds.

STORK   But can't you see that I am not a crane!

FARMER   What do you mean?

STORK   Look at my feathers. They are not like the others. Look! I'm not a crane, I'm a stork!

FARMER   But you came to my field to eat my seeds.

STORK   No! No! NO! I was just passing by and paused to rest. I never eat seeds. I like fish. I'm a stork, not a crane!

FARMER   Maybe so. Maybe so. However, all I know is that you were with the cranes who rob my field of seeds, and you must die with them!

Moral   Be careful of the company you choose.

Suggestions for staging
An imaginary net will be fine.
The birds should use the whole room as they
fly toward the field.
When caught in the net, the birds should make
a strong effort to struggle free.

The Lion
and the Mouse

Characters   A Lion
A Mouse
First Hunter
Second Hunter
Third Hunter

Setting   The lair of a sleeping lion.

MOUSE   I see a tiny piece of food near the mighty lion's paw. Do I dare risk trying to get it? Mr. Lion seems to be sound asleep, and I am very hungry! Yes, I will risk it!
The mouse very carefully creeps near the food,

but suddenly the lion slaps his paw right down on the little mouse.

LION   Now I have you, my little mouse.

MOUSE   Please, oh please, Mr. Lion, have mercy upon a little mouse.

LION   Why should I? You will make a tasty morsel.

MOUSE   Oh, Mr. Lion, I am so tiny. I truly am not worth eating.

LION   Yes, you do seem to be quite tiny.

MOUSE   A mighty lion such as you deserves a bigger mouthful than just a little, little, little mouse.

LION   Yes, I guess you are right. Be gone and don't enter my lair again, for next time I really will gobble you up!

MOUSE   Oh, thank you, thank you, thank you! You are a very generous lion. Thank you, thank you!

LION   Stop thanking me and get out of my lair so I can go back to sleep.

MOUSE   Yes, Mr. Lion.

The mouse scampers out of the lion's lair.

LION   What a silly little mouse. Well, back to sleep. (*He begins to snore loudly.*)

FIRST HUNTER   That lion is really sleeping soundly.

SECOND HUNTER   Listen to his heavy snores.

THIRD HUNTER   Do we dare risk trapping him?

FIRST HUNTER   I don't know. I don't know.

SECOND HUNTER   Let's move closer and see how fast asleep he really is.

THIRD HUNTER   Move very quietly!

The three hunters slowly creep up to the entrance of the lair.

FIRST HUNTER   Listen to those snores!

SECOND HUNTER   He is snoring so loudly that it almost shakes the trees!

THIRD HUNTER   I think we should take a chance and capture him. What do you think?

FIRST HUNTER   Let's try it!

SECOND HUNTER   Get the net ready!

THIRD HUNTER   Are we ready?

FIRST HUNTER   Yes!

SECOND HUNTER   Yes!

THIRD HUNTER   Let's go!

Slowly the hunters enter the lion's lair and wrap the net around the lion.

LION   Help! Help! Help!

FIRST HUNTER   No sense struggling, Mr. Lion. You can't escape from our strong net.

SECOND HUNTER   Let's rush back to the village and get some of our neighbors to help us carry the lion in.

THIRD HUNTER   Everyone in the village will be very proud of us for catching such a big strong lion. *The hunters leave for the village.*

LION   HELP! HELP! HELP! Somebody help me! HELP! HELP!

MOUSE   That sounds like Mr. Lion's voice.

LION   HELP! HELP! HELP! Please help me!

MOUSE   It *is* his voice!

LION   HELP! HELP! I'm trapped! HELP! HELP! HELP!

MOUSE   I'm coming, Mr. Lion! I'm coming!

LION   Oh little mouse, look at the mess I'm in. I

can't get loose from this powerful net that the three hunters cast over me. What shall I do?

MOUSE   I can help you.

LION   You can help me? How?

MOUSE   With my strong sharp teeth I can gnaw a big hole in the net, and then you will be able to escape.

LION   Please try.

The mouse gnaws and gnaws and gnaws and finally the lion is free.

MOUSE   There! I told you I could free you.

LION   Thank you, little mouse. You really are a friend.

MOUSE   Good-bye, Mr. Lion.

Moral   Sometimes good things come in small packages.

Suggestions for staging
The lion should snore loudly.
His lair can be under a table.
The hunters should be extremely careful approaching the lion's lair.
The net can be an imaginary one or a blanket.

The Mules
and the Robbers

Characters   First Mule
Second Mule
First Robber
Second Robber
Third Robber

Setting   Along a country road.

FIRST MULE   My two saddlebags are full of jewels and gold! The master chose me to carry the most valuable saddlebags. Poor you! All you carry in your two saddlebags is dusty grain.

SECOND MULE   I guess I'm not as lucky as you, but I do my job as best I can.

FIRST MULE   I'll say you aren't lucky. I can walk with my head erect and proud, and everyone notices me! Poor you! Nobody, but nobody, looks at you.

SECOND MULE   Yes, you are right. Nobody notices me. All I carry is two dusty bags of grain.

Three robbers creep up to the nearby bushes.

FIRST ROBBER   Let's go over our plan again. I will jump on the proud mule and hit him over the head with my heavy club.

SECOND ROBBER   As you hit the proud mule, I will grab the bag of jewels.

THIRD ROBBER   And I will grab the bag of gold.

FIRST ROBBER   I will keep hitting the proud mule on the head, but remember to work quickly.

SECOND ROBBER   What about the other mule?

THIRD ROBBER   No need to bother about him for he is only carrying two dusty bags of grain.

FIRST ROBBER   Are you ready?

SECOND ROBBER   Ready!

THIRD ROBBER   ATTACK!

The three robbers carry out their plan and run away.

FIRST MULE   Poor me! Oh, how my head hurts! Poor me! Those robbers didn't touch you at all!

SECOND MULE   I guess I was the lucky one this time!

FIRST MULE   Poor me! Boo-hoo, Boo-hoo, Boo-hoo!

Moral   It does not pay to show off.

Suggestions for staging
The proud mule should truly be very proud.
When the robbers attack the proud mule, there can be much noise and confusion.

Two Travelers
and a Purse

Characters   First Traveler
Second Traveler
First Man
Second Man
Third Man

Setting   A path in the countryside.

FIRST TRAVELER   Look! There is a purse in the middle of the road. It's a very heavy purse! Maybe it's full of gold! Yes! Yes! It *is* full of money. How lucky I am! Oh, how lucky I am!

SECOND TRAVELER   Just a moment, my friend. Don't you think you should say how lucky *we* are?

FIRST TRAVELER   Oh no! *I* found it, and it's all mine! Every piece of gold is mine, mine, MINE!

SECOND TRAVELER   But aren't we friends, and are we not traveling together? Shouldn't we share our good fortune as well as our bad fortune?

FIRST TRAVELER   No! No! No! *I* found the purse, and it's all mine! Is that clear?

Three men run shouting down the road.

FIRST MAN   Hey, you there! Stop!

SECOND MAN   Stop thief!

THIRD MAN   Help us catch the thief!

FIRST TRAVELER   I'm frightened! Those people are carrying big sticks and seem very angry.

SECOND TRAVELER   Yes, they are very angry and they are carrying big clubs!

FIRST TRAVELER   We are in a very bad situation! If they find the purse upon us, they will think we stole it instead of just finding it.

SECOND TRAVELER   Just a moment! Don't say *we* are in a bad situation. Remember you just said that the purse was all yours. You would not say *we* before, so don't use the word *we* now!

Moral   If you don't share your good fortune with a friend, don't expect a friend to share your bad fortune.

Suggestions for staging

The men with clubs and sticks should be at the far end of the room pretending they are far down the road.

The children can add any ending they choose to the play, i.e., chasing the traveler, catching him, or the traveler dropping the purse and running away.

175

The Fox
and the Cat

Characters   A Fox
A Cat
A Hunter
First Hound Dog
Second Hound Dog

Setting   In the middle of a forest.

FOX   Do you know something, Mr. Cat?

CAT   What are you talking about?

FOX   I'm much more clever than you are. Do you
realize that?

CAT   I don't exactly know what you mean.

FOX What I'm saying is that I know more tricks than you do.

CAT That probably is true, for I don't know many tricks. In fact, I only know one trick.
Sound of a hunter's horn and the barking of hound dogs.

FOX What was that? What was that noise?

CAT That sounded like the horn of a hunter and the barking of his hounds.

FOX Do you suppose that they are after us?

CAT Possibly.

FOX What shall we do?

CAT Well, I am going to show you the only trick I know and run up this tree to safety.
The cat runs up the tree.

FOX But I don't know how to climb trees. What shall I do, Mr. Cat?

CAT Well, you bragged about having so many tricks. Let me see some of them.

HUNTER There's the fox standing near the tree. Catch him, my beautiful hound dogs.
The hounds chase the fox and catch him.

Moral One positive deed is better than a hundred promised ones.

Suggestions for staging
A desk or a chair on a table can serve as a tree. The hounds can bay and bark as they chase the fox about the room.

The Donkey
in the Lion's Skin

Characters   A Donkey
A Deer
A Snake
A Hawk
A Fox

Setting   Deep in a forest.

DONKEY   Well, look what I just found! The skin of a lion! My, this must have been a big proud lion at one time. I think I will have some fun with this lion skin. I'll put it on and wander about scaring all the creatures of the forest. It will be great, great fun!

The donkey puts on the lion's skin and begins to frighten the creatures of the forest.

Hello, Mr. Deer. You had better start running for I am a wild lion and I am going to eat you up!

DEER   Oh my! I'm so frightened!

The deer runs quickly away.

DONKEY   Ha-ha-ha-ha-ha-ha-ha! I certainly fooled that silly deer. . . . Who else can I frighten? . . . Hello, Mr. Snake. I am a ferocious lion, and you had better crawl away as fast as you can or I will chew you up!

SNAKE   I'm going! I'm going!

The snake crawls away as fast as he can.

DONKEY   Ha-ha-ha-ha-ha-ha-ha! I never saw a snake crawl so fast in all my life. Ha-ha-ha-ha-ha-ha! This is great fun! I think I will now frighten Mr. Hawk. . . . Hello, Mr. Hawk. You had better fly away quickly, or I will pounce upon you and that will be the end of you!

HAWK   Good-bye Mr. Lion!

The hawk flies up into the sky and far away.

DONKEY   Ha-ha-ha-ha-ha-ha-ha-ha-ha-ha! Oh, my stomach hurts from laughing so much! Ha-ha-ha-ha-ha! Hello, Mr. Fox. You look so very frightened of me.

FOX   No, I'm not frightened of you! Why on earth should I be afraid?

DONKEY   What do you mean? Of course you are frightened of me because I'm a wild ferocious lion. Don't you see my shaggy mane and my long tail? All the other animals in the forest are afraid of me.

FOX   I was frightened of you until you opened your big mouth, and then I realized you were not a ferocious lion but a stupid donkey. Even though you are wearing a lion's skin, you cannot disguise the sound of your donkey voice. Good-bye, Mr. Donkey in a lion's skin.

Moral Don't pretend to be something you aren't.

Suggestions for staging
A blanket will be fine for the lion's skin.
Much lion roaring from the donkey as he approaches each animal.
Use the entire room as each animal scampers away.

Plays for Six Students

The Miller, His Son, and Their Donkey

Characters   A Miller
His Son
First Woman
Second Woman
First Man
Second Man

Setting   Along a village road leading toward the city. The miller and his son are walking beside their donkey.

FIRST WOMAN   Well, if this isn't a silly sight! I never saw two such foolish fellows as you!

MILLER   What do you mean, old woman?

FIRST WOMAN   Why are you two walking beside your donkey when one of you could be riding the strong animal?

MILLER   Thank you, old woman, for your kind advice. You ride on the mule, my son, and I will walk alongside.

SON   Yes, father.

FIRST MAN   That is a disgrace! A real disgrace!

MILLER   What are you talking about, old man?

FIRST MAN   As I have always said, there is no respect shown to old age these days.

MILLER   Please explain more clearly what you mean, old man.

FIRST MAN   Get off that donkey, young man, and let your poor, tired father ride!

MILLER   Thank you for your advice, old man. Get off the donkey, son. You walk and I will ride.

SECOND WOMAN   I can't believe my eyes!

MILLER   What is it you can't believe, old woman?

SECOND WOMAN   How do you have the nerve to ride the donkey when your poor little boy can hardly keep up?

MILLER   Thank you for your advice, old woman. Get up on the donkey with me, my son.

SON   Yes, father.

SECOND MAN   You two should be ashamed of yourselves!

MILLER   What do you mean, old man!

SECOND MAN   I will tell you what I mean. Your poor donkey looks so tired and yet you two sit upon

him with smiling faces. You both look so much
stronger than your donkey that I should think
it would be easier for you to carry him.

MILLER   Thank you for your advice, old man.

The miller and his son get off the mule, tie his
legs together, and carry him by placing a pole
between his legs. After a while the donkey be-
comes so uncomfortable in that position that he
attempts to free himself and in doing so breaks
the rope, falls into a river, and drowns.

SON   Boo-hoo! Boo-hoo! Our donkey is dead!

MILLER   Poor me! Poor me! Yes, our donkey is
dead!

Moral   To attempt to please everyone is impossible.

Suggestions for staging
The donkey can be a desk or a chair.
A window pole or stick can be used to carry the
desk.
Much crying at the end of the play.

The Hawk
and the Pigeons

Characters   Father Pigeon
Mother Pigeon
A Hawk
First Baby Pigeon
Second Baby Pigeon
Third Baby Pigeon

Setting   The home of the pigeons.

MOTHER PIGEON   Father Pigeon, Father Pigeon, come quickly to the window!

FATHER PIGEON   What frightens you so, Mother Pigeon?

MOTHER PIGEON   Look way up into the sky.

186

FATHER PIGEON   I don't see anything frightening.

MOTHER PIGEON   Keep looking! Keep looking!

FATHER PIGEON   Yes, I now see what you mean. It looks like a huge eagle.

MOTHER PIGEON   What shall we do? How will we protect our three baby pigeons!

FATHER PIGEON   We will have to find someone to help us.

MOTHER PIGEON   Who? Who?

FATHER PIGEON   Look! There is a hawk in that nearby tree. Let me ask him if he will help us protect our darling baby pigeons from the eagle who might attack at any time.

MOTHER PIGEON   Yes, that's a good idea.

FATHER PIGEON   Mr. Hawk! Mr. Hawk!

HAWK   Yes, Mr. Pigeon, what seems to be the trouble? You seem very upset.

FATHER PIGEON   I am very upset and need your help. Do you see that huge eagle way up in the sky?

HAWK   Yes, I see him.

FATHER PIGEON   Well, he just might attack our darling baby pigeons, and I was wondering if you would kindly enter our home to protect us from that huge eagle.

HAWK   Certainly. I will be delighted to enter your home and be of some help.

MOTHER PIGEON   Oh thank you, thank you, Mr. Hawk!

The hawk flies into the home of the pigeons.

HAWK   How old are you, little baby pigeon?

FIRST BABY PIGEON   I am just one year old.

HAWK   Well, well, well, just one year old. You must be nice and tender so I think I will eat you up. *With one gulp the hawk eats the first baby pigeon.*

MOTHER PIGEON   Oh dear! Oh dear! Oh dear!

FATHER PIGEON   Oh dear! Oh dear! Oh dear!

HAWK   And how old are you, my little pigeon?

SECOND BABY PIGEON   I am also one year old.

HAWK   I am still quite hungry so I will eat you up, too!

With one gulp Mr. Hawk eats the second baby pigeon.

MOTHER PIGEON   Oh dear! Oh dear! Oh dear!

FATHER PIGEON   Oh dear! Oh dear! Oh dear!

HAWK   And how old are you, my pretty little sweet young pigeon?

THIRD BABY PIGEON   Just one year old, too.

HAWK   Good! And I will eat you too!

With one gulp the hawk eats the third baby pigeon.

MOTHER PIGEON   Oh dear! Oh dear! Oh dear!

FATHER PIGEON   Oh dear! Oh dear! Oh dear!

HAWK   And now that the eagle is gone and I have protected you from him, I will say good-bye. *The hawk flies out of the pigeons' house.*

MOTHER PIGEON   Boo-hoo! Boo-hoo! Boo-hoo!

FATHER PIGEON   Boo-hoo! Boo-hoo! Boo-hoo!

Moral   Avoid a cure that is worse than the disease.

Suggestions for staging
Much cooing by the baby pigeons in the pigeons' house.
The mother and father pigeons should be very upset as the hawk gulps down the baby pigeons. The hawk should use the whole room when he flies away.

The Wolves
and the Sheep

Characters   First Wolf
Second Wolf
First Sheep
Second Sheep
Third Sheep
A Dog

Setting   A meadow where some wolves are talking to some sheep.

FIRST WOLF   It's silly that we can't be friends.
SECOND WOLF   Why is there always warfare between us?

FIRST SHEEP   Wouldn't it be nice if we really could be friends.

FIRST WOLF   That is exactly what I'm talking about!

SECOND SHEEP   Yes, but the dog that watches over us does not trust you, Mr. Wolf.

SECOND WOLF   He is the one who causes all the problems.

FIRST WOLF   He always barks at us when we come too close to you. And all we want to do is to be friendly.

THIRD SHEEP   He barks to protect us from you.

FIRST WOLF   Yes, the dog is to blame for placing evil thoughts in your minds.

SECOND WOLF   We don't want to harm you. All we want is your friendship.

FIRST SHEEP   Perhaps what you say is true.

FIRST WOLF   Of course we are telling the truth.

SECOND SHEEP   Well, tell us then what we should do.

SECOND WOLF   The best thing for you to do is to tell the dog to go home and that you don't need him anymore.

FIRST WOLF   If we are going to be friends, why do you need a dog to protect you?

THIRD SHEEP   That makes sense to me.

SECOND WOLF   Go ahead and tell the dog to go home.

FIRST SHEEP   Dog! Dog! Go home. We don't need you anymore.

DOG   Are you sure?

SECOND SHEEP   Yes, we are sure! Go home!

THIRD SHEEP   Go home! Go home! Go home!

The dog wanders home.
As soon as the dog is out of sight, the wolves pounce upon the sheep and gobble them up.

Moral Don't dismiss your friends if they are criticized by your enemies.

Suggestions for staging
The dog can bark as the wolves and sheep talk. When the wolves attack the sheep, use the whole room for much running about.

The Fox
Who Lost His Tail

Characters   Red Fox
         Brown Fox
         Gray Fox
         Black Fox
         White Fox
         Old Fox

Setting   A trap; a fox is caught by his tail.

RED FOX   Oh dear, my tail is caught in a trap. What
   am I to do? Someone come and help me before
   the hunter returns. HELP! HELP! HELP!
   . . . I guess nobody hears me. What am I to do?
   Why did I attempt to steal those young chicks?
   If I had minded my own business, I wouldn't

be in this mess! I guess the only thing I can do now is to pull and pull and pull and hope I can free my tail.

He pulls and pulls and pulls and finally frees himself.

At last I am free! But, oh, poor me! I have lost my tail. . . . I look so silly without a tail. All my friends will now laugh at me. What shall I do? What shall I do? . . . I know what I will do! I'll call a meeting of all the foxes and tell them a few things. (*He begins to yell.*) ATTENTION ALL FOXES OF THE FOREST! SPECIAL MEETING TODAY OF ALL FOXES IN THE NEIGHBORHOOD! SPECIAL MEETING OF ALL FOXES!

All the foxes gather for the meeting called by the red fox.

BROWN FOX   I think we are all here, Red Fox.

RED FOX   Then I will tell you why I called this special meeting.

GRAY FOX   Hurry and tell us.

WHITE FOX   I am very curious.

RED FOX   I wanted to tell you how happy a fox I am without a tail.

BLACK FOX   Are you really happy not having a tail, Red Fox? I must say you look rather strange without a tail.

RED FOX   Oh yes, Black Fox, I am very, very happy without a tail.

WHITE FOX   Can you tell us why, Red Fox?

RED FOX   Certainly I can.

OLD FOX   Well begin, for we are all interested and listening.

RED FOX   Well, first of all I can move about much easier now. Look how easily I turn around. You should try to lose your tails and be as lucky as I am!

The red fox shows the other foxes how easily he can move about.

BROWN FOX   You do that very well, Red Fox.

GRAY FOX   Yes, very well indeed.

WHITE FOX   You do seem to move easily without a tail.

OLD FOX   Give us another reason why we should attempt to lose our tails and be like you. I'm still not convinced.

RED FOX   Why, without a tail it is much easier to creep through holes and jump over fences to get away from the hounds.

BLACK FOX   That could be very true.

BROWN FOX   There is something to what you say.

GRAY FOX   I agree that a tail can be a nuisance some-times.

RED FOX   And, of course, without a tail there is less chance of getting caught in a trap.

WHITE FOX   Like you did?

RED FOX   Exactly as I did.

OLD FOX   You give us many reasons why we should remove our tails, but I don't believe you, Red Fox.

RED FOX   What are you talking about, Old Fox?

OLD FOX   If you had a chance to get your tail back,

you wouldn't be so interested in urging us to lose our tails. No, Red Fox, you can't fool me, and I don't think you will be able to fool the other foxes either.

ALL THE FOXES Good-bye, Red Fox. We are going to keep our tails.

Moral Envy of others always shows.

Suggestions for staging
Much fun can be had with an imaginary tail in an imaginary trap.
Foxes should come from all the directions in the classroom for the special meeting.

The Sick Stag

Characters   A Sick Stag
             A Jackal
             A Rat
             A Fox
             A Raven
             An Ox

Setting   A corner of a pasture where the sick
          stag is resting. He is surrounded by
          food left by his cousin stag to help him
          get well.

JACKAL   Hello, Mr. Stag, I just dropped by to see
how you are feeling.

STAG   Not too well. Not too well, I'm afraid. But it
was nice of you to come by and visit.

JACKAL   It's the least a friend can do. My, isn't that
a tasty bit of meat you have there. Do you mind
if I taste it? It looks so good!

STAG   You may taste it.

JACKAL   Thank you, I will!

The jackal eats up all the meat.

Well, I hope you feel better soon. Good-bye.

RAT   Hello, Mr. Stag. I just dropped by to see how you are feeling.

STAG   Not too well. Not too well, I'm afraid. However, it was nice of you to drop by for a visit.

RAT   It's the least a friend can do. My, isn't that a nice piece of cheese you have there. Do you mind if I just take a tiny taste? It looks so nice and soft.

STAG   You may taste the cheese.

The rat eats up all the cheese.

RAT   Well, I hope you feel better soon, Mr. Stag. Good-bye.

FOX   Hello, Mr. Stag. I just dropped by to see how you were feeling.

STAG   Not too well. Not too well, I'm afraid. However, it was very nice of you to drop by and visit.

FOX   That is the least a friend can do. I'm so thirsty and your water looks so deliciously cool. Do you mind if I just take a small sip?

STAG   You may have a sip.

The fox laps up all the water.

FOX   Well, I hope you feel better soon. Good-bye.

RAVEN   Hello! I just dropped by to see how you are feeling.

STAG   Not too well, I'm afraid. But it was very nice of you to come by and visit.

RAVEN   It's the least a friend can do. Say, those berries you have there certainly look bright and juicy. Do you mind if I eat one of your berries?

STAG   You may have a berry.

The raven gobbles up all the berries.

RAVEN   Hope you will be better soon. Good-bye!

OX   I just dropped by to see how you are feeling.

STAG   Not too well, I'm afraid. However, it was most kind of you to take the time to come to visit.

OX   It is the least a friend can do. Say, that straw you are resting on looks so fresh and clean. Do you mind if I have a small taste?

STAG   You may have a mouthful of the straw.

The ox eats up all the straw the stag is resting upon.

OX   I hope you feel better very soon. Good-bye.

STAG   All my friends came to visit, and now I am left with absolutely nothing . . . no food, no water, and not even my straw to rest upon. Boo-hoo-hoo. Boo-hoo-hoo.

Moral   Calling yourself a friend does not make you one.

Suggestions for staging

When arriving and leaving each child should impersonate the animal he is representing.

Each animal can eat the food belonging to the stag with a great deal of noise.

199

The Milk Woman
and Her Pail

Characters   Milk Woman
First Stranger
Second Stranger
Third Stranger
Fourth Stranger
Fifth Stranger

Setting   Along a country road.

FIRST STRANGER   Where are you going, woman, with
that pail of milk on your head?

MILK WOMAN   I am going to market to sell my milk,

and with the money I am going to buy three hundred eggs.

FIRST STRANGER   Good luck!

MILK WOMAN   Thank you.

SECOND STRANGER   Where are you going, woman, with that pail of milk on your head?

MILK WOMAN   I am going to market to sell my milk, and with the money I am going to buy three hundred eggs and those three hundred eggs will become three hundred chickens.

SECOND STRANGER   Good luck!

MILK WOMAN   Thank you.

THIRD STRANGER   Where are you going, woman, with that pail of milk on your head?

MILK WOMAN   I am going to market to sell my milk, and with the money I will buy three hundred eggs that will become three hundred chickens. Then I will sell the three hundred chickens and buy myself a pretty new gown.

THIRD STRANGER   Good luck to you!

MILK WOMAN   Thank you, stranger.

FOURTH STRANGER   Where are you going, woman, with that pail of milk on your head?

MILK WOMAN   I am going to market to sell my milk for money, and with the money I will buy three hundred eggs that in time will become three hundred chickens. Then I will sell the three hundred chickens for a pretty new gown to wear to the Christmas party!

FOURTH STRANGER   Good luck to you!

MILK WOMAN   Thank you, stranger.

FIFTH STRANGER   Where are you going, woman, with that pail of milk on your head?

MILK WOMAN   I am going to market to sell my milk for money, and with the money I will buy three hundred eggs that in time will turn into three hundred chickens. Then I will sell the three hundred chickens for a pretty new gown to wear to the Christmas party.

FIFTH STRANGER   Well, you certainly have many plans.

MILK WOMAN   Yes, I do! And when I am at the Christmas party and all the boys propose to me, I will shake my head and say NO! I will shake my head just like this!

The milk woman shakes her head, and her milk pail falls to the ground spilling all of the milk.

Moral   Don't count your chickens before they are hatched.

Suggestions for staging
A book could be the pail of milk.
When the milk woman meets the five strangers, they should be in various parts of the room.
When the milk pail falls, the milk woman can cry and wail.

The Shoemaker
Turned Doctor

Characters   A Shoemaker
First Villager
Second Villager
Third Villager
Fourth Villager
Fifth Villager

Setting   A small village.

SHOEMAKER   I haven't sold a pair of shoes in over a month. This is terrible! I guess I'm not a very good shoemaker. I think I will become something else. What shall it be? What shall it be? . . . I know! I will become a doctor. I will go to another village and tell everyone that I am a famous doctor.
The shoemaker locks up his store and walks to another village.

FIRST VILLAGER Someone told me you were a famous doctor. Is that true?

SHOEMAKER Yes, very true. I am a famous doctor.

SECOND VILLAGER What makes you such a famous doctor?

THIRD VILLAGER I never heard of you before. How come you say you are famous?

SHOEMAKER Listen, my friends, and I will tell you. I have invented a medicine that will cure you if you ever are poisoned!

FOURTH VILLAGER Is that really true?

SHOEMAKER Absolutely true, my friend.

FIRST VILLAGER I will buy a bottle of your medicine.

SECOND VILLAGER I will buy a bottle, too.

THIRD VILLAGER Me, too!

FOURTH VILLAGER Are you sure it works?

SHOEMAKER Absolutely sure! Why, only last week I cured a woman who was bitten by a very poisonous snake. My medicine cured her in two minutes!

FOURTH VILLAGER Really! I will buy two bottles!

FIRST VILLAGER I will take another bottle!

SECOND VILLAGER Me, too.

THIRD VILLAGER Give me another bottle, too.

SHOEMAKER Sorry, my friends, I have just sold the last bottle, but I will be back tomorrow with many more bottles.

All the villagers leave for their homes.

A scorpion comes along and bites the shoemaker.

HELP! HELP! HELP! I have just been bitten

by a scorpion. I have been poisoned. HELP! HELP!

FIFTH VILLAGER   Well, well, well, our famous doctor is sick. Here! Drink some of your own medicine and be cured.

SHOEMAKER   NO! NO! NO! My medicine will make me worse. I am not really a doctor. I was just pretending.

FIFTH VILLAGER   Get out of this village and never come back!

The villagers throw the medicine at the shoemaker as he runs away.

Moral   You can fool people some of the time, but you can't fool them all the time.

Suggestions for staging

When the villagers chase the shoemaker out of town, they can throw paper cups at him.

The shoemaker should moan and groan when he is bitten by the scorpion.

The Bowman
and the Mountain Lion

Charácters   A Rabbit
A Deer
A Snake
A Mountain Lion
A Bowman
A Fox

Setting   In the mountains.

RABBIT   Beware, everyone! Here comes a bowman.
I'm leaving!

DEER   The bowman is a very dangerous hunter. Beware, everyone. I'm running away.

SNAKE   Everyone, beware, and get out of here for the bowman is within striking distance.

MOUNTAIN LION   I am not going to leave. I will stay and challenge the hunter.

SNAKE   You are a very foolish mountain lion. You are wasting your time challenging a bowman.

MOUNTAIN LION   Why? Tell me why!

SNAKE   You will find out soon enough mountain lion. I am leaving immediately!

The snake and all the other animals run away.

MOUNTAIN LION   Here I am, bowman, and I am not afraid of you! I am staying right where I am!

BOWMAN   Very well, mountain lion, I will send you a messenger, and it will tell you how dangerous I am!

The bowman shoots an arrow at the mountain lion and wounds him.

MOUNTAIN LION   HELP! HELP! I am wounded. I, too, am leaving here.

FOX   Don't run away, mountain lion. Be brave and stay. Face the bowman again.

MOUNTAIN LION   I am not listening to your advice. If he can send such a dangerous messenger, imagine how dangerous he himself must be. No, I am running away right now!

Moral   A man who can strike from a distance is a dangerous neighbor.

Suggestions for staging
The bowman can create any sound he desires to give the impression of an arrow flying through the air.

As the animals scurry away, they should express much fear. They can use the whole area of the classroom to hide.